SO-AJE-859

A Note from Your Teacher

More Than 450 Notes for Communication and Personalizing Report Cards

by Kimberly Colen

illustrated by Darcy Tom

Teaching & Learning Company

1204 Buchanan St., P.O. Box 10
Carthage, IL 62321

This book belongs to

_____

To Barbara Young, Jackie Caster and Bill Korbus—
three long-time, long distance friendships sustained by letters and notes.

Cover by Darcy Tom

Copyright © 1995, Teaching & Learning Company

ISBN No. 1-57310-033-1

Printing No. 98765432

Teaching & Learning Company
1204 Buchanan St., P.O. Box 10
Carthage, IL 62321

The purchase of this book entitles teachers to make copies for use in their individual classrooms, only. This book, or any part of it, may not be reproduced in any form for any other purposes without prior written permission from the Teaching & Learning Company. It is strictly prohibited to reproduce any part of this book for an entire school or school district, or for commercial resale.

All rights reserved. Printed in the United States of America.

Table of Contents

Part 1: Communication with Parents Made Simple

Part 2: Communication for Report Card and Assessments

TLC10033 Copyright © Teaching & Learning Company, Carthage, IL 62321

Part 3: Communication with Students Made Simple

Part 4: Communication with Administrators and Caretakers Made Simple

Dear Teacher,

As far back as I can remember, I have always enjoyed writing letters. The letters I wrote in first grade to my grandmother remained taped to her wall until the day she died. I recall in second and third grades, that passing letters to friends during class got me into trouble and created much embarrassment when they were discovered and read aloud. To this day, I keep up a correspondence with a friend made during sleep-away camp, when I was ten. At sixteen, my next-door neighbor and best friend moved away, and we have written one another ever since. When I moved to New York after college, one of my most inspiring professors and I wrote to each other. Each letter he wrote was filled with great advice and often signed, "Uncle Bill." We still keep in touch by mail.

Now as a professional writer, I write letters to colleagues all the time. I must have written one too many to the Teaching & Learning Company when the editor called me one day and asked me to write a book of letters for teachers. At once, I thought it was a terrific idea. A teacher has so little time nowadays to do her job as well as to write notes to those she needs to; and of course, effective communication to students and their parents is essential for academic and behavioral growth. I thought about all the people who aren't like me, the people who don't enjoy writing letters, and realized that if I wrote a book of model letters that would make a teacher's life more convenient, the book could really make a difference for you as educators.

And so this book was created for the teacher who wants to say the right thing with a sensitively worded letter at his fingertips. This book was created for the teacher who wants to be clear with her explanation the first time around. This book was created for the teacher who needs to reprimand yet still inspire. This book was created for the teacher who needs to apologize appropriately.

This book will be a long-time companion for all your correspondence needs—there are more than 450 notes inside! If you can't find a letter you need, please write to me, and when this book is updated, we'll add to it! Good luck—and enjoy!

Sincerely,

Kimberly Colen

TLC10033 Copyright © Teaching & Learning Company, Carthage, IL 62321

How This Book Will Help You

If you want to communicate with parents early on in the school year by writing letters, but feel that your words are unclear, disorganized and don't really convey exactly how you feel, this book will help you out! There are more than 450 model letters, notes, invitations, greetings, thank-yous, requests, personal messages, ways to praise, styles of discipline and much, much more.

This book will assist you in effective communication with parents, your students and other school administration. A good teacher knows that early in the school year, letting parents know that you are concerned about and committed to their child's well-being says that your attitude is one of care and responsibility. Communicating with parents is extremely beneficial, not only when things are going smoothly—your child made the honor roll—but also when difficulties arise that need to be approached with tact and diplomacy—why your child may need to be held back a grade. Getting to know parents and caretakers and building a strong relationship right from the beginning of the year, works to everyone's advantage—yours, the parent's and the child's. With some families, and open line of communication may take time, but

remember, small advances are the beginning of what can turn into a growing relationship.

This book is divided into four sections. Part 1 includes notes to send specifically to parents. Part 2 includes short notes to use for report cards or in your own communication with parents describing their child's school behavior. Part 3 includes notes to give your students. Part 4 includes notes to various school administrators and personnel.

The model letters are perfect time-savers. You should find one for every purpose necessary to guide you throughout the year. Use your imagination and creativity to embellish these letters. By simple communications and the hands-on materials in this book, you can help mold the lives of your young students in a way that will benefit them throughout the rest of their lives.

TLC10033 Copyright © Teaching & Learning Company, Carthage, IL 62321

How to Use and Personalize the Contents

You can use this book in many ways. The easiest is to simply make a copy of the page you need—on white or colorful bond paper—and fill in the appropriate person's name. Sign your name, date the message and viola! A completed note in minutes.

Another way to use the notes is to copy a note and use it as your starting point. Add a sentence or two, take out a sentence or two, and create a personal version in your own words. We recommend that you do this for the report card messages. The mix-and-match approach will be most suitable for individualizing your comments.

You can also hold creative classroom lessons using the pages of this book as a starting point. These lessons are designed to help build reading and oral skills—if letters are read aloud, promote self-esteem, encourage creative group and individual projects and help children improve their written communication skills. Following are a few suggestions.

• When children have accomplished a grand feat—or if they must be disciplined—have them write a note home to their parents or caretakers explaining what they have done.

• Ask students to write a note in response to one they received—either from you, from a family member or from a friend.

• Have students design their own stationery with fancy borders, illustrations or both. Then have each one write something about themselves and post these personality profiles on the bulletin board. Allow everyone to get to know one another better.

• Allow children to write a note to a favorite author. Find the name and address of the publisher and send the note there.

2

Making report cards and assessments personal can be challenging. You want the parents to know you are concerned without being critical. You want to express what each child excels in as well as those subjects or behavioral issues in which the child could improve. You want to be as clear as possible without offending anyone.

In "Communication for Report Cards and Assessments" on page 143, there are suggestions for almost every situation you need, whether it be praising a student for being cooperative; disciplining a student for breaking rules or letting a parent know his child is good at expressing himself through art, yet still needs work on spelling–you'll find it in this section.

Keep in mind that it is easy to send a disciplinary note home when something is wrong and remember to send a positive message home when everything is going well. Each student needs as much encouragement as possible–especially the ones who are the most difficult. The more you are involved with parents, the more you and your students will get out of a school year.

Why Parental Involvement Is Important

Dear Parents:

I want your child to enjoy coming to school each and every day. I want to make your child's classroom environment a pleasant one, filled with rich experiences, challenging projects, loads of achievements and lasting friendships.

In order to accomplish this task, I feel it is particularly important to develop and maintain a year of classroom involvement with you. You will be the first to know whether your child is enjoying school, whether your child needs special attention in a specific subject or whether your child's relationship with a friend is affecting his academic development. My commitment to your child is genuine and our interaction is essential to your child's education—both academically and behaviorally.

It is important for us to build a strong relationship with one another for several reasons. Some of the most important are:

- To motivate your child
- To build self-esteem in your child
- To reach common goals together
- To work through difficulties that may arise
- To see that your child enjoys the mental, physical and social activities at school
- To see that your child reaches personal fulfillment
- To nurture and support your child
- To see that your child learns and becomes responsible

Thank you for your cooperation and for your involvement. I look forward to getting to know you and working together in the best interest of your child. If you have any questions throughout the year, please contact me by note or at the phone number below.

Sincerely,

_____
Teacher

_____
Date

_____
Number where I can be reached

_____
Hours available

TLC10033 Copyright © Teaching & Learning Company, Carthage, IL 62321

Learning About You

Dear Parents:

In order for your child to maintain a sense of cohesion between the home and school, I would like to know how you handle various situations. Please fill in the bottom portion of this note and return to me as soon as possible. Thank you for your assistance.

Sincerely,

_____   _____
Teacher   Date

Please fill in and return at your earliest convenience.

Student's name: _____

Parent's name: _____

Does your child discuss school with you? Yes _____   No _____

How do you get your child to talk about school? _____

_____

_____

_____

_____

How do you handle homework in your home? _____

_____

_____

_____

_____

How do you get involved in your child's homework? _____

_____

_____

_____

TLC10033 Copyright © Teaching & Learning Company, Carthage, IL 62321

How often does your child read? _____
_____

How often do you read together—and for how long? _____
_____

Is there a story that your child likes to read over and over? _____

Which one? _____
_____

Are there any problems I should be aware of? _____ What are they?
_____
_____

How does your child react to discipline? _____
_____

What method of discipline reaches your child best? _____
_____
_____
_____
_____

Which method of communication works best for you:

——————— booklet or journal between you and I

——————— parent/teacher conferences

——————— attending school parent nights

——————— notes home/on report cards

——————— parent volunteer programs

6

Learning About Your Child

Dear Parents:

I want to get to know your child better. Please fill out the bottom portion of this form, and return to me at your earliest convenience.

Sincerely,

_____

Teacher   Date

Please fill in and return at your earliest convenience.

Student's name: _____

Birthday: _____

Any siblings? _____ How many? _____ What ages? _____

Your child's favorite activities: _____

_____

After-school activities: _____

_____

Hobbies: _____

_____

Favorite subjects: _____

_____

Best kind of environment to work in: _____

_____

Most difficult environment to work in: _____

Personality traits: _____

_____

Other comments: _____

_____

_____

TLC10033 Copyright © Teaching & Learning Company, Carthage, IL 62321

My Homework Policy

Dear Parents:

You and I both want your child to do well in school. We also want your child to do his best when it comes to homework. I will be giving homework assignments throughout the year. Please go over this note with your child so that you both will be familiar with the policies in my class. My goal is to create a sense of responsibility in each student so that he or she performs to the best of his or her ability.

When homework is not done, _____

_____

When homework is forgotten, _____

_____

When homework is incomplete, _____

_____

When homework is unacceptable, _____

_____

When homework is sloppy or messy, _____

_____

When homework is missed, _____

_____

_____

When your child is sick, homework will be handled

_____

_____

_____

Sincerely,

_____

Teacher

_____

Date

TLC10033 Copyright © Teaching & Learning Company, Carthage, IL 62321

My Discipline Policy

Dear Parents:

Throughout the year I will use discipline to maintain order and control as necessary. Although my classroom will have a flexible learning atmosphere, I offer the following guidelines of acceptable behavior that will be enforced throughout the year. Your child deserves the best educational environment possible.

Please review the information below with your child.

For unruly or unmanageable behavior, _____

_____

For repeated disruptive behavior, _____

_____

For fighting, _____

_____

For pranks, _____

_____

For breaking rules, _____

_____

For repeated absence, _____

_____

For (other): _____

_____

If you have concerns about the above measures, I suggest we get together to discuss the form of discipline that will work and be most appropriate.

Sincerely,

_____

Teacher

_____

Date

TLC10033 Copyright © Teaching & Learning Company, Carthage, IL 62321

* Part 1 *

Communication with Parents Made Simple

This section includes more than 125 notes to send home to parents with your students. Some notes are for everyday matters such as establishing good homework patterns and reading activities to do together. Other notes are reminders about the importance of a hug or about an upcoming television program that you feel would be special for your students to watch. There are notes that will be difficult to send home such as holding a child back a year and after-school detention; and notes about matters you will be delighted to share with parents, like a good progress report or an honor roll achievement.
In this section you will find a note diplomatically asking for anything you may need throughout the year. You will find an invitation for every occasion and you will find a personal greeting for parents or anyone else you choose to send one to.

Save loads of time and effort by finding the letter you need to send to your student's parent or parents—and never worry about what to say again!

TLC10033 Copyright © Teaching & Learning Company, Carthage, IL 62321

The First Day of School

Dear Parents:

During the first day of school we:

_____ made new friends
_____ shared about ourselves
_____ located the bathrooms
_____ located the cafeteria
_____ other: _____

_____

Your child: _____

_____ plunged right into school life
_____ enjoyed the day's activities
_____ missed you
_____ took the separation hard
_____ other: _____

_____

_____

1ST DAY OF SCHOOL

I will be in touch with you throughout the year to keep you informed about your child's academic and behavioral performance.

Sincerely,

_____   _____
Teacher   Date

TLC10033 Copyright © Teaching & Learning Company, Carthage, IL 62321

The Importance of Talking and Listening

Dear Parents:

Does the following conversation sound familiar:

Parent: "How was your day?"
Child: "Fine."
Parent: "What did you do in school today?"
Child: "Nothin'."
Parent: "How was the trip to the history museum?"
Child: "OK."

This may sound like a great conversation to some parents, and to others it may sound like your child has tuned out bothersome questions.

Let's take a look at the importance of really talking and really listening. In order to do that, we must add the importance of really hearing and really understanding.

In order to really talk to your child, it is important that you look directly at him. Your child's body language will give you more answers to how he feels than what he says. Look at the expression in his eyes. Look at his posture and see whether his muscles seem tense or calm. Look at his hands—are they clinched or relaxed?

As you listen and observe your child, concentrate on what he is actually saying. Sit or stand close to him. Allow him to express the things that are important to him without interruption. Listen courteously. If he won't communicate, be sensitive to the times when he is more receptive to talking.

Two of the things that don't work are nagging and threats. So why do we use them as tools to motivate our children? Because they are easy. It's not easy to really communicate—it takes lots of practice and work to get better and better.

As a suggestion, one of the best ways to have a conversation with your child is to stop asking "Why?" Some children are intimidated by the question. Instead, use a phrase like, "You seem angry. Something must have happened today." Or, "I can see that you are frustrated. Your homework must be difficult." Communicating in this manner encourages a child to open up in a nonthreatenting, nonnagging way.

12

Once your child opens up . . .
- hear what is said
- understand the feelings that go with the comment. Instead of getting the last word in or reacting with a gasp, take time to care about how your child is feeling.
- don't cut off your child. He may go back to answering your questions in one-word sentences. Your intention is to know what is going on in your child's private world.

Using the above steps will help you achieve this.

In review, to communicate with your child, you must look at him, listen to and hear what is said and understand. Please let me know how this method of communicating works for you.

Sincerely,

_____   _____
Teacher   Date

The Importance of Establishing Good Homework Patterns

Dear Parents:

You have the unique opportunity to have a positive affect on your child's future. The development of homework patterns begins in childhood and shapes how your child will work throughout life. It is important that you help your child establish good homework habits that he can take with him well into adult life.

Here are eight things you can do to set a healthy homework tone:

1. Find an appropriate place to do schoolwork. Select a well-lit, comfortable, quiet spot in your home, and make that a designated homework area.

2. Find a quiet area without distractions. A place without a television, radio or stereo is optimal. Make sure this spot is away from others who are not doing homework.

3. Either find a place that is well-lit or create an area with a lot of light. Poor lighting creates eye fatigue.

4. Make sure the area has the necessary supplies close at hand. (See list of supplies on the next page.)

5. Establish routine study hours. Find a good time to do homework, and have your child study within this time frame every day.

6. Encourage your child to do his best work and to get it done on time. Do not do the homework for your child. If there is something he doesn't understand, guide him through the directions in order that he reach the goal himself.

7. Praise your child's efforts—not only when he brings home a good grade but for small efforts as well.

8. If your child is not doing his homework, listen to why and then communicate firmly that you expect him to be a responsible student and get his homework to school when assigned.

Remember, what you do to create a homework policy in your home today, will set the tone for how your child works tomorrow.

Sincerely,

_____   _____
Teacher   Date

TLC10033 Copyright © Teaching & Learning Company, Carthage, IL 62321

Supplies to Keep in the Study Area

Dear Parents:

Here is a list of supplies to keep close at hand. The grade level most appropriate is mentioned next to the item.

pencils (all grades)
pens (3-up)
markers (all grades)
writing paper (all grades)
construction paper (all grades)
tape (all grades)
glue (all grades)
eraser (all grades)
pencil sharpener (all grades)
scissors (all grades)
children's dictionary (1-3)
crayons (1-6)
assignment book (2-up)
folders (2-up)

Sincerely,

_____
Teacher

_____
Date

Easy-to-Make
Do Not Disturb Sign

Dear Parents:

As an afternoon activity, help your child make this door sign.

Materials:
scissors
cardboard
glue
colored construction paper
crayons or markers

Steps:
1. Copy, color and cut out the image on the right and glue to an 8¹/₂" x 11" (21.6 x 27.94 cm) piece of cardboard.
2. Cut dotted line through to circle and cut out hole.
3. Put on doorknob and watch no one disturb you!

Have fun!

Sincerely,

_____
Teacher

_____
Date

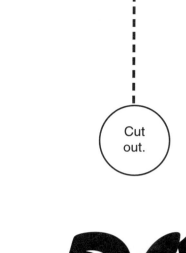

DO NOT DISTURB!

16

A Homework Hit!

Just a message to tell you that

_____

did an excellent job on the homework assignment

last night   this week

_____

_____

Teacher: _____

Date: _____

---------- Cut here. ----------

_____ Is a Homework Hero!

This champion _____

_____

_____

Thank you for all of your support!

Teacher:_____

Date: _____

---------- Cut here. ----------

_____
teacher

is proud of

_____

for doing an EXCELLENT job on homework!

Teacher: _____

Date: _____

Homework Happenings!

A Message from the Teacher

To: _____ Date: _____

From: _____

_____

_____

_____

_____

_____

_____

- Cut here and send back with reply. -

A Reply from the Parent

To: _____ Date: _____

From: _____

_____

_____

_____

_____

_____

TLC10033 Copyright © Teaching & Learning Company, Carthage, IL 62321

SCHOOL ATTENDANCE

Dear Parents:

I want to make school an exciting experience for your child, one that he will look forward to every day. I plan to use programs that will enrich your child's life and motivate him to want to come to school. It is important that your child attend school every day, and I ask that you help in the following ways:

- If you plan a vacation or out-of-town visit, do so when school is not in session.
- Have your child at school on time.
- Arrange for your child to be at school every day, even when it is inconvenient for you to take him.

- _____

_____

Should your child not want to come to school because of various reasons (anything from a problem with peers to anxiety about an oral report or not being able to go to the bathroom as needed), please notify me, and I will see how I can make the situation more comfortable for your child.

Thank you for your cooperation.

Sincerely,

The early bird catches the worm

_____
Teacher

_____
Date

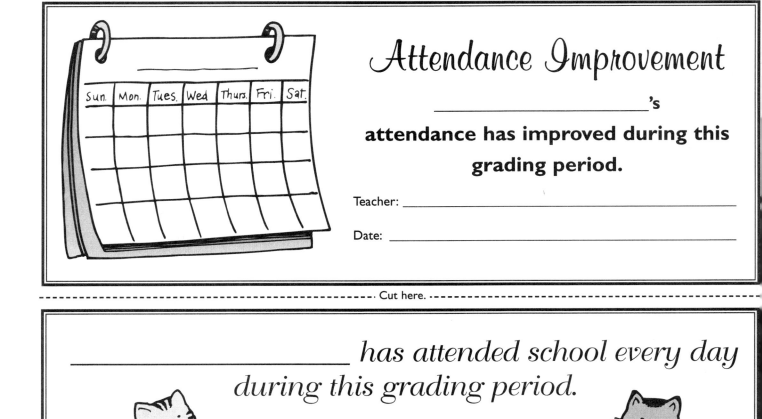

Attendance Improvement

_____'s

attendance has improved during this grading period.

Teacher: _____

Date: _____

-- Cut here. ---

_____ *has attended school every day during this grading period.*

EXCELLENT WORK!

Teacher: _____   Date: _____

-- Cut here. ---

_____,

your attendance is

100%

this week!
Congratulations!

Week# ____
Monday ☑
Tuesday ☑
Wednesday ☑
Thursday ☑
Friday ☑

Teacher: _____

Date: _____

TLC10033 Copyright © Teaching & Learning Company, Carthage, IL 6232

DISPLAYING WORK

Dear Parents:

Every child is thrilled to see his work displayed. In the classroom, we are able to display work and awards on the bulletin board and by decorating walls.

It is a good idea to display your child's work at home, too. Having a picture, award, report card, note or assignment that you are particularly proud of may be just the encouragement your child needs to keep up the good work he is putting forth. An exhibit of artwork and special assignments is motivation for your child to continue to expose his creative ideas.

Find a space on the refrigerator, cabinets or walls, or make a special space for displaying work. This helps your child know you value his work. It also builds self-esteem.

Each child wants to please a parent and knowing you are interested in her work is a motivating factor in her educational development. Take pride in your child's efforts–no matter how small. Post good news such as an honor roll listing, a good grade or first place ribbon so that everyone can see–and make this display area come alive and grow with color, creativity and more and more good work.

Sincerely,

_____   _____
Teacher   Date

Helping Your Child Build a Positive Attitude

Dear Parents:

Being a good role model is important for your child. As your child grows up, he sees and emulates your way of thinking whether it be of school, work, chores or anything else, so it is important that it be positive. Here are just a few things you can do to assure a positive attitude:

- Listen, hear and understand others and their feelings.
- Try new things and allow your child to do the same.
- Be accepting of others.
- Don't compare one person with another.
- Foster independence and develop a sense of responsibility.
- Spend as much time with your family as possible, both at work and at play.
- Do things as a family that give you a chance to praise and enjoy one another.
- Emphasize the positive.

- _____
  _____
- _____
  _____
- _____
  _____

Sincerely,

_____   _____
Teacher   Date

TLC10033 Copyright © Teaching & Learning Company, Carthage, IL 6232

The Importance of a Hug

Dear Parents:

Hug your child every day. This simple concept is an important gesture, and the physical embrace is a way of connecting with your child. Children who feel loved and cared for have high self-esteem and do well in their endeavors. Young children have a need to be loved and cuddled, especially by the adults they live with. And guess what—it will do you as much good as it does your child. Remember, there's always time to fit in a big hug!

- Do be aware that if your child gets used to hugs from home and then goes off to school (and expects a teacher to give hugs) where the teacher may show affection differently, this does not mean that the teacher doesn't like your child. It means the teacher has a different style than the one your child is used to.

On the left is a sign to cut out and post on a wall, on your refrigerator or next to your daily calendar. This will help everyone in your family remember the importance of a hug.

Sincerely,

_____
Teacher

_____
Date

The Importance of a Good Breakfast

Dear Parents:

Your child needs to be alert all morning during school or his performance will suffer. One way to achieve this is to see to it that he gets a good breakfast in the morning before he is sent out the door. Providing your child with a steady routine is helpful and important. When a child is rested and fed, he is ready to get involved in daily activities. Proper food is necessary for good health. Food provides the nourishment a body needs in order to grow.

If your child ever tells you that he is draggy during the late morning, it may just be that he needs a bigger breakfast.

Please see that your child always gets a good, nourishing breakfast. Examples of healthy breakfast foods are listed below.

Carbohydrates give energy:
fruits, breads, rolls

Proteins are building blocks for the body:
milk, cheese, eggs, lean bacon or Canadian bacon

Minerals help form bones and teeth:
milk, dried fruits

Vitamins help make you grow:
milk, fruit juices, breakfast cereals, bread

Sincerely,

_____   _____
Teacher   Date

24

TLC10033 Copyright © Teaching & Learning Company, Carthage, IL 6232

The Importance of a Good Night of Sleep

Dear Parents:

When your child has a good night of sleep, he performs better and is ready to take on his daily activities as well as new things that may arise. When your child has not had a good night of sleep, he is less able to perform academically, his behavior becomes difficult and he is more susceptible to germs that can cause illness.

Have your child do his homework in the afternoon or early in the evening. It can often become an unpleasant situation if he puts off the assignment until right before bedtime. At this time he is tired and cannot do as good a job as when he is completely awake and absorbed (and you're tired of nagging by now, too).

If you have a child that requires less sleep, ask him to go to his room and lie quietly or read a calming book before going to sleep.

There are many reasons why your child needs a good night of sleep:

- Your child will perform better academically during school hours.
- Your child will be able to handle a new and unfamiliar situation should it arise.
- Your child's mind is clear and fresh.
- A body works best when it's had a good night of sleep.
- You will have time for yourself at the end of the day.

Please see that your child gets a good night of sleep—for everyone's sake.

Thank you!

Sincerely,

_____   _____
Teacher   Date

S. _____

The Importance of Good Grooming

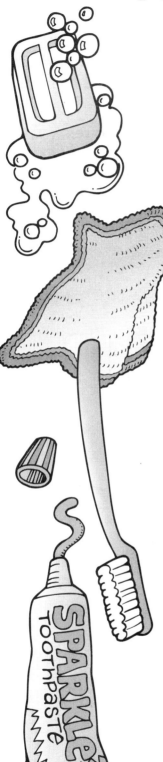

Dear Parents:

When your child is groomed well, he feels better and has a greater amount of self-esteem. He is also able to keep and maintain friends. Being social and fitting in is important to a person's mental health. Keeping your child and his surroundings clean, helps protect him against diseases caused by germs.

Before coming to school each day, see to it that your child:

- takes a bath using soap and water
- brushes his teeth
- brushes his hair (and washes it on a regular basis)
- is wearing clean underclothes

Creating a set of routine hygenic standards will be invaluable to your child throughout his lifetime. By keeping clean, staying well-groomed and playing in clean surroundings, a child will remain healthy and feel better on the whole—both in his appearance and in his attitude.

Sincerely,

_____

Teacher

_____

Date

TLC10033 Copyright © Teaching & Learning Company, Carthage, IL 623

The Importance of Good Posture

Dear Parents:

Your child's body looks more graceful and works best when he has good posture. Good posture makes a person look tired all the time. It causes stiff muscles, sore necks and backaches. Have your child stand with his feet firmly on the ground. When he walks, make sure his toes are pointed straight and knees are slightly bent. Hold the stomach in—this helps keep the back straight. Shoulders are to be straightened, also. Head high, chin in—now everything is in line.

A surefire way of testing good posture is to have your child lean against a wall. If his feet, head, shoulders, legs and buttocks touch the wall, his posture is good.

By walking, sitting and standing straight, your child will look better and feel comfortable. Check out your child's posture today!

Sincerely,

_____

Teacher

_____

Date

Reading Together

Dear Parents:

Help your child become a lifelong reader. By reading together at home, you can open the doors to many places and different worlds. Reading together is a valuable activity and one that is basic to education. You can share opportunities with your child, watch his growth and become a partner in his education. As your child watches you or older siblings read, or as you read together, he is more likely to become a reader himself. By reading together, you can help your child toward a successful future.

Here are some of the opportunities reading together offers:

- It's fun, it's entertaining and it's informative.
- Children do better in school and become better students.
- A book is a conversation starter. Your child is more likely to open up to thoughts and feelings relating to the subject being read.
- It gets a child thinking and predicting, "What will happen next?"
- It allows children to learn new words and have larger vocabularies.
- It allows you to share important and valuable moments with your child.
- It promotes feelings of success as your child explores language.

TLC10033 Copyright © Teaching & Learning Company, Carthage, IL 62321

In the next letter, you will find activities that will help you become a true partner in the exciting venture your child is about to embark. Have fun, go at a pace your child is most comfortable with and enjoy the process all the way!

Sincerely,

_____   _____
Teacher   Date

-- Cut here. --

The family of _____ enjoys reading together because

_____

_____.

_____   _____
Signed   Date

Great Reading Activities

Dear Parents:

There are so many ways and so many places to share a good book. You can share a book in your home, under a tree, in a secret hideout, when you're on vacation or in bed just before bedtime.

Here are some ideas:

- After reading a book, share what it was about.
- Pretend you are the author and tell why you wrote the book.
- State three things you learned after reading the story.
- Tell how you would change the ending of the book.
- Think up a different way for the main character to solve his or her problem.
- Read the book to a younger sister or brother.
- Make a cassette recording of you or your child reading the story. Let others listen to the tape, while following along in the book. (Send to Grandpa and Grandma.)
- If the book could talk, what would it say about itself?
- Tell another story about the main character.
- Draw things that you see in the book.
- List the three best parts of the book.
- Make up a poem about the book.
- Role-play one of the characters.
- Dress up as one of the characters.
- Draw what happens in one scene.

...and Queen Sarah reigned throne...

30

Do you have a favorite reading activity or ways you share a book together? Fill in the note below and return it to school. When you come in, I will introduce you to ways other families share books. Thank you for your time.

Sincerely,

_____   _____
Teacher   Date

-- Cut here. --

Reading Power

Please fill in and return to school with your child.

Our child is _____.

In our family we share a book by _____

_____

Our favorite books are_____

_____

_____

Our favorite reading activity is _____

_____

_____

Selecting a Book for Your Child

Dear Parents:

There is such a large selection of books for children these days—how do you know which ones to choose to read to your child? Your objective as a parent is to get good books into the hands of your child, books that you think her will like. How do you know which book will strike the cord and turn her on to something new, something creative or something that will capture her imagination?

Here are some hints in selecting a book for your child:

- Find books relating to the hobby and interests your child enjoys. A good book in that particular subject matter will not only entertain your child but will be educational as well.

- Bring your child along—to the library or bookstore—when picking out a book. The more he takes an active interest in the project, the more interested he will be to read the book.

- Find books with pictures, even if your child thinks the book looks like a "baby" book. The pictures help spark discussions, they unlock the imagination and they promote creative storytelling.

- Select a book you enjoyed as a child and read it aloud with excitement and familiarity. Most likely, with this enthusiasm, your child will enjoy it, too.

- Select books that have gold and silver awards on them. Award-winning titles are selected by their content and are usually very safe bets.

TLC10033 Copyright © Teaching & Learning Company, Carthage, IL 62321

- Select ones that are fun for you to read. The more animated you sound when reading, the more fun your child will have listening, and the experience will be enjoyable for you both.
- Select a book that links a child to his everyday world. If you have just baked cookies and the characters in the story are baking cookies, you can relate the experience to one your child has just had, making the story more real.

Remember, you can always ask a librarian or bookstore owner to direct you to books you and your child might take home and enjoy. They are there to help you with your specific needs and goals.

Sincerely,

_____   _____
Teacher   Date

-- Cut here. --

ANY BOOK SELECTING IDEAS?

Please fill in and return to school with your child.

Our child is _____.

The way we select books is by_____

_____

_____

Activities for Becoming a Better Reader

Dear Parents:

There are many activities you can do with your child to help him to become a better reader. As a matter of fact, they are so much fun, you won't believe they're activities for learning! Most of the activities are simple and can be done anywhere.

Here are some ideas:
- Think of a word and see how many times your child can find it in the newspaper or a magazine—or if in a car, on the signs you pass.
- When you are in the car, point out a sign and see if your child can read it.
- Let your child read the advertisements that come in the mail.
- Have your child help you cook by reading a recipe.
- Have your child help you create a project by reading the directions involved.
- Have your child help you select which cereal to buy in the grocery store by reading the boxes.
- Have your child help you find where you are going by looking in the phone book for the address.
- Have your child help you do the laundry by turning the knobs on the washer and dryer.
- Have your child apply for his own library card.
- Have your child learn how to play a game by reading directions aloud.

Have fun!

Sincerely,

_____   _____
Teacher   Date

TLC10033 Copyright © Teaching & Learning Company, Carthage, IL 62321

BETTER READER IDEAS?

Any ideas, parents? Please fill in and return to school with your child if you have something to share with us.

Our child is _____.

We have found that one way of becoming a better reader

is to _____

_____

_____

_____

_____

_____

_____

TLC10033 Copyright © Teaching & Learning Company, Carthage, IL 62321

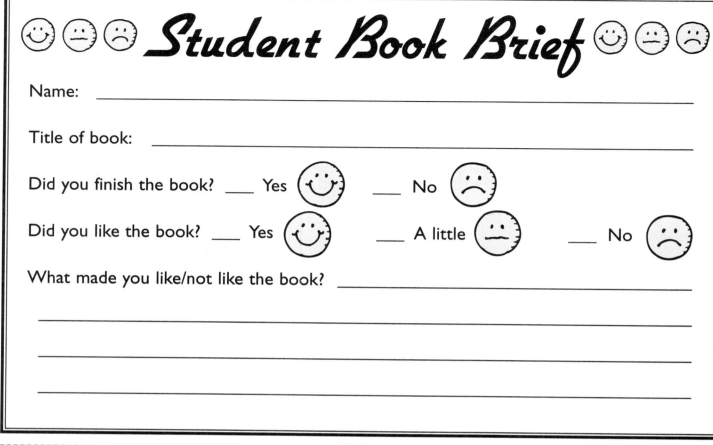

Student Book Brief

Name: _____

Title of book: _____

Did you finish the book? ___ Yes 😊   ___ No 😞

Did you like the book? ___ Yes 😊   ___ A little 😕   ___ No 😞

What made you like/not like the book? _____

_____

_____

_____

- Cut here. -

Reading Contract

I,_____, plan to read
student

_____
title of book

by _____
date

_____
witness

Great Effort

TLC10033 Copyright © Teaching & Learning Company, Carthage, IL 62321

We Couldn't Put This Book Down . . .

_____

title

because

_____

_____

_____

_____

_____

_____
Signed   Date

- Cut here. -

I Read This Book at Home

_____

title

and I Loved It!

It is about . . .

_____

_____

_____

_____

_____
Signed

_____
Date

Vocabulary Building Together

Dear Parents:

"Seize. It means to take by force...to capture..."

One sure way your child can gain a growing vocabulary and find meaning in more words is reading to him every night. Another way for your child to learn vocabulary is to talk to your child often. The more you use words, the more words will show up in your child's vocabulary. If your child has been exposed to rich conversation, the more words he will know.

Allow your child to have many different experiences. The more background your child has for different things in the world, the more words she learns—and the easier time she has of reading. It's fun to learn a new word.

There are several activities that you can do at home to strengthen your child's vocabulary.

- Work on a crossword puzzle book. Make sure it is age-appropriate so that your child does not get discouraged.
- Play Scrabble® together.
- Make learning words a family affair. At the dinner table, have each family member introduce a new word and define it for everyone.
- At the dinner table, try to stump a grown-up by asking him a new word. If the adult knows it, ask him to define it. Then have your child make up a sentence using the new word correctly. If the grown-up cannot define it, have the child define it and use it in a sentence.
- Write vocabulary words on one side of a 3" x 5" (8 x 13 cm) index card. Put the definition on the back. Then ask your child the definition of a word. If he doesn't know the word, allow him to read the information on the back.
- Watch an educational program together. Pick out a few new words that are included in the program and practice using them.
- Start with a short sentence such as, "This is a rose." Have each person playing add another word or two to the sentence—"This is a pretty rose." Then "This is a pretty pink rose found in Grandma's garden."

38

- Take your child to a park, zoo, nursery or greenhouse, drugstore, grocery store, etc. Point out familiar items and animals and say their names while exploring the environment.
- Look at a photo album together, and have your child recall the event, the place and the people. Start a discussion.

These ideas should provide you with hours of activities to enjoy together.

Sincerely,

_____   _____
Teacher   Date
- Cut here. -

Any ideas, parents? Please fill in and return to school with your child if you have something to share with us.

Our child is _____.

We have found that one way of increasing our vocabulary is to _____

_____

_____

Spelling Together

Dear Parents:

As your child gets more and more involved in reading, she will eventually become curious about spelling. Here are some fun, high-interest activities to help practice spelling at home.

- Spelling Puzzle: Write each letter of a word on a piece of cardboard. Then cut the letter into puzzle pieces. Allow your child to piece together the letters and then the word!

- On small index cards, write about 20-30 words you want your child to learn. Then have your child alphabetize the cards. Once the alphabetizing becomes easy, staple cards together to create a small spelling book.

- Make a cassette tape of 20-30 spelling words. After saying each word, spell the word, spell the word slowly. Or, if your child is proficient at spelling, have him make the tape in his own voice by spelling the words.

- Matching Game: Use 3" x 5" (8 x 13 cm) index cards and write the same word on two cards. Do this with 10-15 words. (You will then have a double amount of cards.) Turn all cards facedown and have first player pick up two cards. If they match, player takes them out of the game and turns up two more cards. If they don't match, return them to the facedown position and the next player takes a turn. Whomever has the most cards in their stack wins the game.

- Play the word game Hangman. It's a great way to learn words while having fun.

- Get a magnetic alphabet and put the letters on the refrigerator. Use this when relaying a short message to your child and have him do the same.

- Have your child copy words you have spelled on paper. Then have him draw a picture to go with each word.

TLC10033 Copyright © Teaching & Learning Company, Carthage, IL 62321

- Have your child write and illustrate a story. Don't worry about spelling mistakes if your child is making an effort. Let him read it to you and to other brothers and sisters.

Be sure to have fun along the way.

Sincerely,

_____   _____
Teacher   Date
--- Cut here. ---

Any ideas, parents? Please fill in and return to school with your child if you have something to share with us.

Our child is _____.

We have found that one great way of learning to spell is to _____

_____

_____

_____

_____

TLC10033 Copyright © Teaching & Learning Company, Carthage, IL 62321

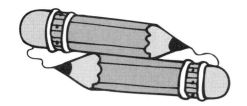

Writing Activities Together

Dear Parents:

To reinforce writing activities done in school, here are activities you and your child will enjoy at home together.

- Write a note for your child and put it in a place it will be seen. Ask for a written reply.
- Ask your child to write down the items he needs at the grocery store or drugstore, and have him go with you to get the items.
- Ask your child to write a note to a grandparent or friend who lives in a different city, state or country. (This activity will be especially exciting if your child receives a letter in response.)
- Make some artistic stationery with several small pictures or one big picture. Add lines and have your child write a note to someone special with this stationery.
- Tear pictures from a magazine and ask your child to write a caption for each one.
- Keep a parent/child journal with an ongoing dialogue. Leave and pick up messages in this journal.
- Have your child help you label things in the freezer, in your desk, on the bathroom shelves, etc.

There are so many exciting writing activities. Anything from a note that says "Hi" on the breakfast table in the morning, to a "Good night" note on your child's pillow at the end of the day. Be clever and think up other writing activities for the rest of the day. Siblings enjoy assisting because there is excitement in these activities for the whole family.

Sincerely,

_____   _____
Teacher   Date

42

Any ideas, parents? Please fill in and return to school with your child if you have something to share with us.

Our child is _____.

We have found a great writing activity to be _____

_____

_____

_____

_____

TLC10033 Copyright © Teaching & Learning Company, Carthage, IL 62321

Math Together

Dear Parents:

What can be more exciting, stimulating and challenging than learning math? Math helps us in everyday activities such as making a purchase to planning a party, from building a tree house to measuring a cup of cereal. Work with your child on the activities that follow, and you will find her math skills improve with time. Keep in mind that your child will work at a level of his interest and ability.

- When you make a trip to the grocery store for a few items, have your child add up the total bill. Then tell your child that you plan to take back something that is spoiled. Have him figure the bill without the extra item.

- Cook up a storm! When baking brownies together, ask your child to measure the ingredients before adding them to the mixture. Taste the yummy results!

- Find four dice. Make sure three look alike and one looks different—either in size or color. Roll all four dice and see who gets the highest roll. Do this several times, adding up all numbers and then finding the total. Also, roll all four dice, add up the three that are alike and then subtract the number on the die that is different. This is good practice for subtraction.

- Find a catalog and have your child pick three items she would like from the catalog. Add them up and find the total amount to be paid.

- Have your child add up the number of minutes he watches television each day. Change the minutes into hours. Create a list of the total minutes for all week. How many hours does that make?

- Explain coins—pennies, nickels, dimes and quarters. When making a simple purchase, get assistance from your child.

- Fill a money bag with coins and ask your child to count and find out how much is in the bag. If she guesses right, she gets to keep the money!

- If you have a collection of something at home, like buttons or CDs, have your child count the total number in your collection.

+ √ MINUTES = HRS.		
MON.	150	2 1/2
TUES.	120	2
WED.	30	1/2
THURS.	195	3 1/4
FRI.	270	4 1/2
TOTAL	765	12 3/4

TLC10033 Copyright © Teaching & Learning Company, Carthage, IL 62321

- Make up simple stories of addition, subtraction and multiplication. Allow your child time to think of the answer. Make up simple stories having to do with time, too.
- Write a number on a piece of paper. Then around the house or yard, find things that are exactly that number. (Example: 6 light bulbs, 8 flowers, 12 dishes, etc.)

Whatever you do, instill a sense of self-confidence when your child answers correctly. Make sure you apply the problems or story to something your child can relate and apply to his world. The more comfortable your child is with numbers, time and measurements, the better he'll become at math. Be patient—if you want to see results—you will!

Sincerely,

_____   _____
Teacher   Date

-- Cut here. --

Any ideas, parents? Please fill in and return to school with your child if you have something to share with us.

Our child is _____.

We have found that a great way to learn math at home is_____

_____

_____

SCIENCE TOGETHER

Dear Parents:

All children are born with a sense of wonder
and each one needs an adult who can help share
it with them. Be eager to explore, discover,
observe, experiment and learn together! Here
are some ways to do so:

- Catch an insect in a jar, watch it and talk about what you see. Then let it go.
- Find a magnifying glass and have your child observe things laid out underneath the glass. What does she see that is ordinarily hidden from view? (Things to look at include insects, dust, parts of your body, leaves and plants, bread mold, etc.)
- Have your child learn to see, hear, smell, taste and touch to gather information about different objects. What does he learn about salt and sugar by tasting? What does he find out about the scents around the house? What does he find out about a sponge and a nail file after touching these items?
- Give your child various rocks, seeds or leaves. Ask her to sort them by size, by texture, by color, by weight (the rocks). What does she discover?
- Grow mold. Take a piece of fresh bread. Put it on a paper plate and sprinkle it with water. Wrap plastic around it and put it in a dark drawer. Take it out two days later. What has happened? Put the bread back into the drawer and take it out in another two days. Write your observations. Keep track of the mold-growing process. (Remember, molded bread is not for eating!)
- Which float? Which sink? Gather objects like a Ping-Pong™ ball, plastic fork, ruler, scissors, spring, thick rope, balloon, etc. Ask your child which ones he thinks float. Which items does he think sink? Test the items by getting a pan of water and seeing for yourself!
- Take two identical items of clothing—like a pair of socks. Get them both wet, then leave them outside to dry. Put one in the shade and one in the sun. Which sock dries faster? Why?

TLC10033 Copyright © Teaching & Learning Company, Carthage, IL 62321

- Growing sprouts. Get sprout seeds, plant them, set them near your kitchen windowsill and watch them grow. What do you learn from this? What do you find interesting about their growth?
- Go outside and listen—what do you hear? Stay inside and listen—what do you hear? What do these sounds sound like when you tap your ears with the palms of your hands? When you open your mouth wide—and wider? When you turn your head to one side and then to the other side fast?

Science is fun. Children learn to be accurate, learn how to raise questions and use their minds in trying to find answers, learn to be open about different objects, learn to identify and store information and learn from the mistakes they make. When dealing with science and young children, there will be feelings of joy and excitement with the interactions of the world. Remember, if you spot a hazard, make sound rules that are appropriate for your child. Have fun!

Sincerely,

_____   _____
Teacher   Date

- Cut here. -

SCIENCE IDEAS?

Any ideas, parents? Please fill in and return to school with your child if you have something to share with us.

Our child is _____.

We have found that a great way to learn science at home is _____

_____

_____

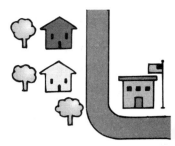

Social Studies Together

Dear Parents:

Understanding oneself in the context of other human beings is what social studies is all about. Recognizing that each of our environments is different, yet each depends on one another is human nature at its best. Try the following activities at home for a greater understanding of the social experience:

- When you and your child are in the car, get close to home and ask your child to give you directions the rest of the way. Ask that he say *left* or *right* and tell you about the distance you need to travel at each turn.
- Look at a map together. Show your child where you live. Then point to different places where relatives and friends live that your child knows. Ask your child to help you measure the distance between different places.
- Ask your child what the weather is like outside. On the way to and from school, make observations about the weather and the season. Discuss the season and its impact on people in your hometown. Go through each season and discuss what kinds of things people do differently, i.e. in winter you wear coats, in summer you wear shorts, etc. Teach your child how to read a thermometer.
- Discuss the possible differences between you and people who live in a different city, state or country. What are the similarities? (Example: weather, transportation, method of housing, etc.)
- Make a map of your home. Make a map of your school. Make a map of your neighborhood. Use symbols for houses, trees, stores, parks, roads, etc. Teach directions from these maps.
- Discuss transportation around your community. What is different and the same between your community and another community? (How do you go to school–walk, bus, car, bike, subway, etc.)
- Talk about your neighborhood. What is good about it? What do you like least about it? What do the neighbors do for one another?
- Compare living in a city versus living in the country. What are the similarities? What are the differences? Ask your child what he thinks he might like and might not like living in a different environment.
- Pantomime different community people doing their jobs. (Examples: farmer milking a cow, firefighter putting out fires, police officer directing traffic, mail carrier delivering letters, nurse taking someone's temperature, etc.)

48

- Have your child interview someone older, preferably a grandparent, and find out what life was like for them when they were the same age as your child.
- As your child lies on the floor, trace him on a large sheet of colored paper. When he gets up, have him color and dress his outline with crayons. Do this with each child and then hang up the large murals. Notice the differences and similarities.

These activities help prepare your child for understanding and participating in the community and world more effectively. With this information, your child is now on his way to being a responsible citizen—in school, at home, on the playground and eventually out in the world.

Sincerely,

_____   _____
Teacher   Date

--- Cut here. ---

ANY SOCIAL STUDIES IDEAS?

Any ideas, parents? Please fill in and return to school with your child if you have something to share with us.

Our child is _____.

We have found that a great way to learn about other people is _____

_____

_____

Art Together

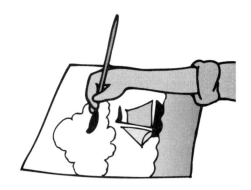

Dear Parents:

Does your child show interest in drawing? Watercoloring? Modeling with clay? Does your child like making murals or ceramics? If your answer is *yes* to one or more of these activities, you may have a budding artist on your hands. Exposure to art in the early grades can begin a lifetime of enjoyment with art.

Here are some activities you can do with your child at home that promote self-expression. These projects can be created simply using homemade materials.

- Make a calendar pinup. Draw a space for a picture and hang a month-at-a-glance calendar below it. Display the calendar in your home where it will get exposure, such as the kitchen or den. Ask your child to draw 12 pictures to fit in the space, then use the calendar for a whole year!

- Put a solid object under a piece of white paper such as a coin, a key, a paper clip. Then rub the top of the paper with a crayon or colored pencil. Watch as the image pops through the paper. Make pictures this way. Experiment on other small, flat items. Do the same thing putting a piece of white paper over a different texture. Watch as the texture emerges on the paper.

- Gather large, smooth rocks. Get some newspaper and paints. Put your rock on top of newspapers, and begin painting it. After the paint dries, put on a clear coating. Give the decorated rock as a gift. It makes a nice paperweight.

- With colored chalk, design an image on a brown grocery bag and use it for a trash receptacle. See what comments this conversation piece receives.

- Tear up pieces of colored construction paper and create a collage out of the torn paper.

- Create a fantastic cut-paper design. Horizontally, fold a sheet of 11" x 17" (28 x 43 cm) paper into four even sizes—fold in a method as if you were making a fan. Then fold this long thin piece in half. Next, cut many small shapes out of the paper until most of the paper is cut out and only

TLC10033 Copyright © Teaching & Learning Company, Carthage, IL 62321

a little of the paper is remaining. Unfold the paper carefully. Mount the design on a piece of colored paper, stand back and admire your work!

- Make seed jewelry. Use a variety of dried seeds and string them along a thread. Tie the ends of the thread together and you have a bracelet or necklace.
- Knead clay into a ball the size of an orange. Use your thumbs to press the clay inward to form a small bowl. Rotate the clay until the bowl is shallow and the walls are all the same width. Use or display.

Because art is not likely to be provided as a requirement, it is up to you to help your child get that extra experience in art. Happy creating!

Sincerely,

_____   _____

Teacher   Date

-------------------------------- Cut here. --------------------------------

Any ideas, parents? Please fill in and return to school with your child if you have something to share with us.

Our child is _____.

We have found a great art project to do at home. It is _____

_____

_____

Fall Together

Dear Parents:

It's fall! The days are getting a little shorter and somewhat cooler. The leaves are turning beautiful shades of orange, yellow, red and brown. Birds are flying South, and squirrels are collecting food for winter. You are probably noticing many more changes around you as well. School is beginning, so during the time you spend with your child, here are some wonderful seasonal activities to do together.

- Make a fall bookmark. Get a piece of cardboard, and glue decorative fall leaves to it. Put two large books on top and let sit for a week until the leaves flatten and dry. Use your bookmark with your favorite book.
- Make a leaf collage. Create a scene with fish, trees, faces and other familiar items. Take notes as to the kind of tree each leaf is from.
- Have your child think of reasons for liking fall. Write them down. Then ask if he likes pumpkin pie and bake one! Ask if she likes playing in the leaves and let her do so. Ask whether he likes watching squirrels or not. If so, allow this.
- Tell your child a story about a fall memory.
- Sing a song about fall together such as "Turkey in the Straw"; "Turn, Turn, Turn" or "To Everything There Is a Season"; "The More We Get Together"; "The Bus Song." Think up more!
- Have your child write what *fall* means to him and draw a picture to accompany it.
- Using your five senses, make five lists of thing you see, smell, touch, hear and taste during the fall season.
- Think of a fall topic such as leaves, school, apples, Halloween, wind, etc., and during dinner, have each member of the family think about what that topic means to him or her.
- Think of something interesting that happened a long time ago during the fall. Discuss the subject and find out more about it. What if this was happening now–how would you feel?

TLC10033 Copyright © Teaching & Learning Company, Carthage, IL 6232

- Clean up! Start a job earning money by recycling, taking out the trash or other household chores. For every quarter earned, put away a nickel. By holiday time, your child can take the money set aside and buy someone less fortunate a holiday gift.
- Cook an autumn meal. Cook carrots; roast turkey; crack nuts for snacks; bake an apple pie.
- Find leaves, small branches and seeds, and create a large picture with these items by gluing them on paper. Frame and hang up.

I hope you will enjoy these activities.

Sincerely,

_____   _____
Teacher   Date

------------------------------------ Cut here. ------------------------------------

FALL PROJECT IDEAS?

Any ideas, parents? Please fill in and return to school with your child if you have something to share with us.

Our child is _____.

We have found a great fall project to do at home. It is _____

_____

_____

Winter Together

Dear Parents:

During the winter season, you may see snow or frost. You'll also see bare trees and few animals or insects. This is a good time for some indoor fun, if the weather is too cold to play outside. Try these activities.

- Create a winter calendar. Draw a weather symbol of sunshine, a cloud, rain or snow for each day of the month of December, January and/or February. If some days need more than one symbol, put as many on as needed. Draw symbols in different colors and see how delightful and colorful the calendar becomes.
- Make snowpeople sugar cookies and decorate with powdered sugar. Add raisin eyes, a red-hot cinnamon mouth and a thin black licorice scarf.
- Color, cut and paste! Make holiday greeting cards for relatives and friends. Send them out early.
- Create a coupon book. Have your child make five coupons such: as stay up 30 minutes later, watch one extra program on television, help make brownies and other things he wishes for and you approve. After the coupons are written and colored, sign them and allow your child to use them whenever he wishes, especially during holiday time.
- Make a bread snowflake. Get one piece of white bread and cut out corners and inside shapes to create a unique shape. Bake at a low temperature 10-20 minutes, until slightly brown. Take out of oven and hang outside for birds.
- Make paper snowflakes and stick on windows to decorate the room. Cut out a circle on white paper. Fold in half. Fold in half again and again. Snip edges in various shapes and carefully unfold. Now decorate and hang outside.
- Fill various size jars with jelly beans, gum balls and other small festive objects. Have your children guess how many are in each jar. The one who comes closest gets the jar and its contents. This makes a great party game.

54

TLC10033 Copyright © Teaching & Learning Company, Carthage, IL 6232

- Scavenger Hunt: Write a note and hide it. When your child finds the first note, have that note explain where to look for a second note. When she finds the second note, it explains where to look for a third note . . . and so on. The final note should have a warm and special message.
- Find 1" (2.5 cm) thick sticks. Strip bark and sandpaper the stick smooth. Next, paint an imaginary creature on the stick with bright colors. Add small bead eyes, tail feathers, yarn hair and give your creature a name.

Have a fun winter!

Sincerely,

_____   _____
Teacher   Date

-- Cut here. --

WINTER PROJECT IDEAS ?

Any ideas, parents? Please fill in and return to school with your child if you have something to share with us.

Our child is _____.

We have found a great winter project to do at home. It is _____

_____

_____

Spring Together

Dear Parents:

Spring means being outdoors, jumping high, enjoying the weather, occasional showers, buds swelling into flowers and animals coming out of their hibernation. Here are some activities you can do indoors or outdoors.

- Carrot tops! Cut the tops (large ends) of carrots off–about 1" (2.5 cm). Put the flat side into a small bowl of water, filled to ¼" (.6 cm) level. Watch! In one or two weeks, you'll see greenery shooting from the tops.

- Sing spring songs such as "Michael, Row the Boat Ashore"; "What Have They Done to the Rain?"; "Eensy Weensy Spider"; "Frog Went a Courting"; "It's Pouring"; "Here We Go 'Round the Mulberry Bush"; "Skip to My Lou"; "A-Tisket, A-Tasket"; "Rain, Rain"; "Six Little Ducks" and any others you think of.

- Spring spelling. Think of 10 words that have to do with spring, such as *basket, showers, growth, insects, blooms*, etc. Write them down and practice spelling them.

- Create a garden by planting bulbs. Get a pot, soil, some water and follow your gardener's directions as to when to water and how much sunlight to give your growing plant.

- Go outside with pencil and paper. Record every small animal or insect that you see and the place where you saw each one. (Find a frog, squirrel, earthworm, ant, fly, cricket, spider and bumblebee–don't get too close to this insect!) What was each creature doing when you spotted it? Did you scare it away, or did it stay around and allow you to watch it?

- On a rainy day try this. Get some colored chalk and draw a design on a piece of white paper. Put the paper outside and watch what happens to the patterns on the picture made by the rain. Be sure to hold down your paper using rocks, so that it doesn't blow away!

TLC10033 Copyright © Teaching & Learning Company, Carthage, IL 6232

Enjoy your spring together. It's a nice time of year for science projects and all kinds of activities.

Sincerely,

_____   _____
Teacher   Date

-- Cut here. --

Any ideas, parents? Please fill in and return to school with your child if you have something to share with us.

Our child is _____.

We have found a great spring project to do at home. It is _____

_____

_____

Summer Together

Dear Parents:

This is the season you will need the most activities to do with your children because they are home more often and will want to stay occupied, so get equipped with these exciting activities:

- "Fan"tastic! Make a fan for someone you love. Color a piece of paper and decorate it with glitter and bright colors on both sides. Then fold it accordion style into a fan. Staple the bottom. Give as a summer gift to someone who's HOT!
- Find and watch a bee collect nectar (be careful and don't get too close), a cricket singing a song, a frog jumping or a ladybug laying eggs on a leaf. What do you notice? What do you learn?
- Go outside, sit under a tree and read a book. Bring a picnic lunch, a blanket and enjoy the day.
- Draw a picture of yourself doing your favorite summer activity.
- If you plan a trip, show your child maps and tour guides as a way to involve him so that he will read all about the place he's going. What is there that will especially interest him?
- Dry flowers for decoration or potpourri. Here's how—pick flowers that have not fully bloomed. Tie five or six stems together and hang upside down in a dark, dry place, such as a cellar or closet. Leave for three weeks, until dried. Carefully take down when they are ready and display.
- Begin a summer journal. Write in it every day.
- Sing summer songs such as "Mr. Sun," "Ring-a-Ring 'o Roses," "If You're Happy and You Know It," "This Old Man" and any others you think of.
- Make sand pictures with stencils. Lay a stencil on a piece of paper and spread glue inside the shape you want to come out on paper. Sprinkle sand inside the shape, pull up the stencil carefully and let dry. Come back 10 minutes later and shake off excess sand. Do this with other stencil shapes.

TLC10033 Copyright © Teaching & Learning Company, Carthage, IL 623

- Decorate a box using shells you've collected. Create your design first by laying the shells on top of the box in the order that you want them secured on the top. Then raise each one long enough to add glue and stick it down. After your project is complete, wait overnight so that the glue is good and dry. Your box is ready to use!

- Feed the ants. Find an ant nest and put different foods nearby such as cookie crumbs, bread crumbs, cheese, a cracker, etc. Which food or foods do the ants go to? Which ones do they stay away from? Find out which foods are ants favorite this way.

See you in school next year. Have an exciting summer!

Sincerely,

_____   _____
Teacher   Date

-- Cut here. --

Any ideas, parents? Please fill in and return to school with your child if you have something to share with us.

Our child is _____.

We have found a great summer project to do at home. It is _____

_____

_____

Setting Up a Phone Conference

Dear Parents:

I think it is necessary for us to set up a phone conference and talk about _____
_____

We will go over the areas your child is doing well in and also take a look at those that need improvement.

I'd like to discuss the following topics:

Work habits at school _____

Study habits at home _____

Attitude _____

Behavior _____

Specific subject area _____

Relations with others _____

Self-esteem _____

Other: _____

_____

Additional comments:_____

_____

_____

Thank you for your cooperation. Please fill in the attached note and return it by_____
_____.

Sincerely,

_____   _____
Teacher   Date

TLC10033 Copyright © Teaching & Learning Company, Carthage, IL 62321

Parents: _____   Child: _____

The best time to reach me for a phone conference is   _____

_____

The number you can reach me at is _____

Comments: _____

_____

_____

_____

- Cut here. -

Confirmation of Phone Conference

I will call you on _____,
                                                    day

_____,
                              date

at _____ a.m./p.m.
              time

_____
                          teacher

Come in for a Conference

Dear Parents:

I think it would be beneficial for you to come in so that we could talk about _____
_____

In order for us to make the best use of our time together, I have filled in this note so that you know beforehand what the matter refers to.

I think it is necessary for us to meet because I am concerned about _____
_____

In order to solve the problem, I have taken the following steps: _____
_____
_____

My solution is _____
_____
_____
_____

I think more action needs to be taken such as _____
_____
_____

Let's make a difference in your child's life—and let's start now! I want to make sure your child takes full advantage of what school has to offer.

Sincerely,

_____
Teacher

_____
Date

TLC10033 Copyright © Teaching & Learning Company, Carthage, IL 62321

Confirmation of Conference

Your conference is scheduled for _____,
day

_____,
date

at _____ a.m./p.m.
time

_____
teacher

---- Cut here. ----

Conference Follow-Up

To: _____   From: _____

I will contact you on _____,
day

_____,
date

at _____
time

to let you know the status of the things we went over together.

DO YOU HAVE A QUESTION?

Dear Parents:

I encourage you to contact me at anytime throughout the year if you have a question about your child's learning abilities, behavior, study habits or anything else you feel you want to discuss. Remember, your care and concern contribute to your child's education.

I can be reached at (   ) _____

during the hours of _____

Sincerely,

_____

Teacher

_____

Date

------------------------------ Cut here. ------------------------------

Three Important Reasons to Contact Me

Dear Parents:

Please contact me if your child ever complains about the following three things:

- that I don't like him or her
- that I am not explaining the work well
- that I've given an unfair grade

I want to be able to discuss these things with your child and know that he is comfortable approaching me with any one of these problems.

Thank you for your cooperation!

Sincerely,

_____   _____

Teacher   Date

TLC10033 Copyright © Teaching & Learning Company, Carthage, IL 62321

Your Child May Be Bored

Dear Parents:

I think your child may be bored in school, because

_____ he has a problem listening

_____ he has a problem paying attention

_____ he may have a learning difficulty

_____ he needs more challenging work

_____ he may be troubled or worried about something other than schoolwork

_____ he is anxious to pursue other activities

_____ other: _____

_____

Please contact me at your earliest convenience so that we may get to the root of the matter. This will permit your child to get involved in an exciting learning program as soon as possible.

Sincerely,

_____   _____
Teacher   Date

Extra Homework

Dear Parents:

You may notice that _____ is coming home with extra homework
    today   tomorrow   next week   other: _____

There is a reason for this.

   _____ There is an additional assignment to do.

   _____ Your child is being punished.

   _____ Your child is doing extra credit work.

   _____ Your child failed to finish the assignment the first time.

   _____ Your child is not turning in his best work.

   _____ Your child is not turning in work at all.

   _____ Other: _____

                       _____

Additional comments: _____

_____

_____

Sincerely,

_____
Teacher

_____
Date

TLC10033 Copyright © Teaching & Learning Company, Carthage, IL 62321

Too Concerned About Popularity

Dear Parents:

I find that your child is overly concerned about being popular. He/She depends upon the approval of his/her peers and often seems he/she can be talked into anything. This type of insecurity can hurt his/her grades and schoolwork. It is important that you take time with

_____ and discuss how he/she sees himself/herself. Children like this may be very smart with a fear of standing out and being different from their peers. As soon as you find out what the real problem is, you can better handle the issue. Please let me know what I can do to help.

I wonder if Henry & Jake think I'm cool enough....

Sincerely,

_____   _____
Teacher   Date

ADD Testing

Dear Parents:

Your child exhibits hyperactive behavior. He has a problem focusing and giving his attention to the person talking, and I suggest that you have him tested for Attention Deficit Disorder or ADD. This can be done either through our school counselor or through an outside psychologist. If you have never had your child evaluated, and you suspect he has at least eight of the following characteristics, your child may have Attention Deficit Disorder, according to the American Psychiatric Association diagnostic manual. These are some symptoms:

- fidgets with hands and feet and squirms around in seat
- has difficulty remaining seated
- easily distracted
- blurts out an answer before a question has been completed
- has difficulty following through on instructions
- shifts from one activity to another without completing the first one
- has difficulty playing quietly
- talks excessively
- interrupts others often
- looses things
- engages in physically dangerous activities without considering the consequences

Please let me know what I can do and how I can be of help.

Sincerely,

_____
Teacher

_____
Date

TLC10033 Copyright © Teaching & Learning Company, Carthage, IL 62321

Think About Having Your Child Tutored

Dear Parents:

There are several signs that indicate your child may need tutoring:

_____ lagging behind in subject

_____ slow at completing tasks

_____ difficulty keeping up because of a poor grasp of the fundamentals previously taught

_____ poor study habits

_____ poor self-esteem in academic abilities

_____ other: _____

Additional comments: _____

_____

Please take a look at the list I've marked above and the comments I've made. Tutoring will help improve your child's study skills in an area where your child is lacking.

Sincerely,

_____   _____
Teacher   Date

-- Cut here. --

Holding Your Child Back One Grade/One Year

Dear Parents:

I think you should consider holding your child back next year and allow him to complete _____ grade again. The reason for this decision is because:

_____ achievement level is low

_____ socially immature

_____ missed schooling due to _____

_____ physical size is small

_____ learning difficulties

_____ unmotivated or uncooperative in schoolwork

If you want to set up a conference and discuss this matter further, please contact me at _____ during the hours of _____ and _____.

Sincerely,

_____   _____
Teacher   Date

10 Reasons Grades Go Down

Dear Parents:

You may be aware of your child bringing home lower grades. He is capable of doing better, and there is probably a good explanation of why his grades have dropped. I think the cause is _____.

Below is a list of 10 reasons grades drop. Please take a look at this list and see if your child's schoolwork is hurting because of one of the following areas:

1. Does your child worry excessively—over schoolwork or personal life? This may take energy away from her work. A little concern is healthy; excessive worry is not.
2. Is your child experiencing a traumatic situation at home, such as a divorce, fighting between parents, illness or death?
3. Is your child experiencing discomfort in school, such as wearing clothing too tight? Is the temperature or noise level too low or too high?
4. Is your child lazy or not able to follow through with a decision? This may stem from negative surroundings, critical friends or relatives. It is counter productive.
5. Is your child unmotivated? If so, he may not have good feelings about his abilities or relationships.
6. Does your child have behavior problems such as arguing with others, aggressiveness or silliness?
7. Does your child suffer emotionally from low self-esteem, being a failure or depression?
8. Does your child not have a focus? If he were to stop doing many things and focus on one activity such as schoolwork, grades would improve.
9. Is your child sick often? Does he have headaches, stomachaches, fevers? Has he missed an excessive amount of school because of this? Does he have too much fun when he is sick at home?
10. Does your child show a lack of interest? Is he dull or listless? Is he uninterested in what he is studying?

Please contact me when you want to discuss this matter further.

Sincerely,

_____   _____
Teacher   Date

TLC10033 Copyright © Teaching & Learning Company, Carthage, IL 62321

THINK ABOUT HAVING YOUR CHILD'S HEARING TESTED

Dear Parents:

If your child appears lazy—this may not be his problem at all! He may be hard of hearing—it's often difficult to tell the difference. Some signs of a hearing problem are:

- your child turns one ear to people who are talking to him, straining to hear
- plays the television or radio louder than others
- asks to repeat sentences often
- has difficulty learning or retaining words
- misses details in oral directions
- responds to written messages more than oral directions
- watches person talking to him closely, as if to lip read
- enunciates poorly
- often shows blank expressions

If your child exhibits any of these symptoms, check out his hearing at a local clinic or ask the school counselor to refer you to a place where hearing is tested. Clear up this matter immediately so that your child can continue his school routine with little or no interruption.

Sincerely,

_____
Teacher

_____
Date

Additional comments: _____

_____

_____

_____

Beep

Think About Having Your Child's Eyesight Tested

Dear Parents:

A vision problem that needs to be diagnosed and corrected is something that should not suspend your child's learning process at all. That's why it is good to act immediately on this matter.

Symptoms of a visual problem are:
- child has difficulty seeing the chalkboard and copying material from it
- child has headaches or sore eyes that are often rubbed
- child holds book close to his eyes to read
- child sits close to television screen to see
- child squints
- child skips lines as he reads
- child cannot read for a long period of time
- child closes or covers one eye to read or focus

C
ATS
ARE THE
BEST
ANIMALS
IN THE LAND

To have testing done in this area, contact a local ophthalmologist or optometrist. Do this as quickly as possible so that your child does not suffer discomfort or pain.

Sincerely,

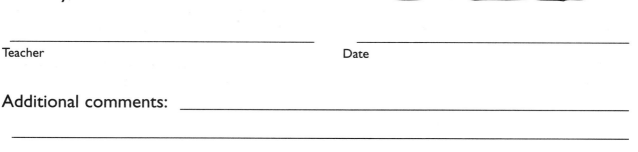

_____   _____
Teacher   Date

Additional comments: _____

_____

_____

TLC10033 Copyright © Teaching & Learning Company, Carthage, IL 62321

Your Gifted Child

Dear Parents:

It is important to raise a happy, well-adjusted child who fits in with his or her peers, and if your child is gifted, this becomes a challenge and a joy because your child is not exactly typical.

If you think your child is gifted in one or several areas, you're probably right. Research shows that parents who can accurately define the behavior of their child are usually correct.

It is my belief that your child may be gifted. I have checked on the chart below the category in which your child exhibits special ability:

_____ intellectual ability (smart in many areas, has a good memory, spends time with older children, has a long attention span, applies concepts of reading and math in contexts other than originally introduced)

_____ specific apptitude for one thing (usually in math, linguistics or science—can focus on this area of endeavor, is a "whiz" in one area)

_____ creative or productive thinker (thinks about things that don't occur to other children, has a creative sense of humor, constantly asks questions, can use description in great detail)

_____ leadership ability (can convince many people to do what he/she wants, offers suggestions to children and have them readily accepted, recognizes when his behavior produces certain results, has a sense of fair play for both himself and others)

_____ ability in the visual or performing arts (has a high potential to dance, sing, draw, play a musical instrument; spends free time working on this talent; has advanced hand-eye coordination; shares feelings and moods through this talent)

_____ motor ability (can play and do well in sports-related games with older children, can balance well on one foot or when hanging from a bar, can use athletic equipment with ease and skill)

To confirm the notion that your child may be gifted, you may want to have him tested by professionals—either in the form of an achievement test or by an I.Q. test. There are two good reasons to test.
1. If you have specific concerns about the educational opportunities available to your child.
2. If your child is having a difficult time in school or having behavioral problems at home. A child who is six but mentally several years older is at odds with herself and the world.

If there is anything I can do to help find the right environment for your child and one best suited to his needs, please let me know. I want your child to achieve everything that's possible.

Sincerely,

_____   _____
Teacher   Date

TLC10033 Copyright © Teaching & Learning Company, Carthage, IL 62321

Your Child May Have a Learning Disability

Dear Parents:

I have reason to believe your child may have a learning disability. Although the causes for learning disabilities are unclear, there are common characteristics of children with learning disabilities. I have checked the one(s) I think apply to your child.

___ difficulty with academic skills (reading, writing and mathematic ability)

___ difficulty with fine motor skills (handwriting and copying from a workbook or chalkboard)

___ difficulty with memory (both long and short term)

___ difficulty with attention spans (too short, easily distracted, moving around)

___ difficulty organizing

___ difficulty making friends and keeping them

___ low self-esteem

___ other: _____

Please note that your child may have difficulty in one of these areas without having a learning disability, however if you feel your child is having trouble keeping up and succeeding in school, you might want to explore this idea. Remember, you play a strong role in making sure your child gets the help he needs.

Be aware that your child can be a successful student even with a learning disability and know that I am prepared to work with you and anyone else in helping your child be the best he can be in school. Let me know what I can do.

Sincerely,

_____   _____

Teacher   Date

-------------------------------------- Cut here. --------------------------------------

I Suspect Drugs

Dear Parents:

I have reason to believe that your child, _____,
may be experimenting with drugs. There are a number of reasons drugs are attractive to children: drugs allow children a reckless self-indulgence; they help children to feel like they are part of a peer group; the sale of drugs allows children to buy things they normally cannot afford.

If you suspect that your child may be taking or selling drugs, reasons could be anything from a lack of self-respect to a cry of despair. Bring the subject of drug use out in the open and discuss it with your child. Seek professional help if the need arises. The sooner you take care of this matter, the better life will be for both you and your child.

Sincerely,

_____   _____

Teacher   Date

TLC10033 Copyright © Teaching & Learning Company, Carthage, IL 62321

Welcome to Town!

Dear _____ :

I look forward to getting to know you and your family. If there is anything I can do for you, please let me know. Feel free to stop by or give me a call.

My room number is _____.

My phone number is (____) _____.

_____ _____
Teacher   Date

----------------------------- Cut here. -----------------------------

Welcome to School!

Dear _____ :

I look forward to having your child in my class. If there is anything I can do to make your child feel more comfortable, please let me know. Please stop by and see what we're up to!

_____
Teacher

_____
Date

TLC10033 Copyright © Teaching & Learning Company, Carthage, IL 62321

ENTERING SCHOOL MIDYEAR

Dear _____ :

Welcome to school! If your child is worried about making new friends, I assure you I will help introduce him to the other children in class. I will see to it that someone in class shows your child around the school. Please encourage your child to actively seek new friends by introducing himself/herself and asking as many questions as he feels he/she needs to be comfortable.

_____
Teacher

_____
Date

-------------------------------- Cut here. --------------------------------

Come Visit Our Class

Dear _____ :

It would be great if you stopped by to see us!

The best days to come are _____

_____ because

_____.

The best times to drop in are _____.

That's when we _____

_____.

We look forward to seeing you!

_____
Teacher

_____
Date

TLC10033 Copyright © Teaching & Learning Company, Carthage, IL 62321

Would You Like to Participate in

_____ ?

Dear _____ :

Please say *yes* because _____

_____ .

Here's how you can take part _____

_____

_____ .

Reply by _____ .

Please fill out and return to school with your child.

- Cut here. -

Name: _____   Child: _____

_____ Yes, I would love to participate in _____

_____

_____ No, I cannot participate at this time.

- Cut here. -

Thank You for Participating in

_____

Your presence made the event delightful for us.

Sincerely,

_____   _____
Teacher   Date

Mistakes Are

OK

Dear _____:

In my class, your child's effort is what counts.

Please remind _____
that trying is more important than doing a perfect job.

_____
Teacher

_____
Date

-- Cut here. --

Look Over This

Dear _____:

Please be sure to notice

_____

_____

_____

_____

Thank you!

_____
Teacher

_____
Date

TLC10033 Copyright © Teaching & Learning Company, Carthage, IL 62321

Progress Report

Student: _____

A (✓) check applies to your child's progress.

Schoolwork
_____ Doing very well, understands concepts
_____ Able to concentrate and get work done
_____ Motivated to do excellent work
_____ Needs assistance
_____ Other: _____

Attitude
_____ Excellent
_____ Good
_____ Fair
_____ Poor

Effort
_____ Tries hard and fully understands
_____ Tries hard but doesn't seem to understand
_____ Could try harder

Your child excels in these areas: _____

_____

_____

Your child is having difficulties in: _____

_____

_____

Additional comments: _____

_____

_____

_____   _____
Teacher   Date

Group Work

Dear _____:

It is important for every child to learn to mature in group activities. For this reason, we will be doing group projects in our class. Our most recent one was _____
_____.

After the project was completed, your child
_____ developed well socially
_____ became emotionally immature when grouped with others
_____ sought to be safe on the sidelines
_____ other: _____

I want to make group work an enjoyable activity for your child.

If you would like to comment on the above evaluation, please do so on the back and return this note to school with your child.

_____   _____
Teacher   Date

TLC10033 Copyright © Teaching & Learning Company, Carthage, IL 62321

Independent Study Projects

Dear _____:

In order that talent and creativity emerge, your child will be given independent study projects. These projects are assigned because of the need for children to learn to work at their own pace. Our most recent independent study project was

_____

After the project was completed, your child was found:

_____ to be extremely responsible working this way

_____ to have the ability but lacks the confidence

_____ that he did not want to do the work on his own

_____ to complain that the work was too difficult

_____ other: _____

_____

If you would like to comment on the above evaluation, please do so on the back and return this note to school with your child.

_____   _____
Teacher   Date

Dear Parents:

In Case of Poor Weather . . .

we will cancel _____

_____

and will reschedule it _____.

Please excuse the inconvenience!

Sincerely,

_____   _____
Teacher   Date

------------------------------------ Cut here. ------------------------------------

Dear Parents:

A Reminder to Resume . . .

the _____

that was cancelled because of poor weather.

New continuation date: _____

Thank you!

Sincerely,

_____   _____
Teacher   Date

TLC10033 Copyright © Teaching & Learning Company, Carthage, IL 62321

School Closing

Just a note to remind you that school will be closed on_____ due to _____. It will resume again on _____.

Sincerely,

_____
Teacher

_____
Date

Cut here.

Dear Parents:

Your child made the

Honor Roll

this grading period.

Congratulations!

_____
Teacher

_____
Date

Special Television Program

Dear Parents:

I recommend you and your child watch

_____

It will be especially beneficial because _____

_____

It will be on television _____, on channel _____.

Enjoy!

Sincerely,

_____   _____
Teacher   Date

TLC10033 Copyright © Teaching & Learning Company, Carthage, IL 6232

Dear Parents:

I want _____ to

Stay After School for
DETENTION

on _____,

from _____ to _____,

in order to _____

_____.

This detention is because _____

_____

_____.

Please plan to pick up your child after
_____ on that day.

I appreciate your cooperation.

Sincerely,

_____
Teacher

_____
Date

LC10033 Copyright © Teaching & Learning Company, Carthage, IL 62321

Dear Parents:

I would like _____ to stay after school for

special participation in

_____

on _____, from _____ to _____.

Please fill out the permission form below and return it

to school with your child by _____.

I appreciate your cooperation.

Sincerely,

_____   _____

- Cut here and return form below to school. -

Special Help

Child: _____

_____ has my permission to stay after school on _____.

_____ cannot stay after school on _____.

_____   _____
Parent   Date

TLC10033 Copyright © Teaching & Learning Company, Carthage, IL 6232

Dear Parents:

Your Child Has Been Injured

Injury: _____

How it happened: _____

_____

Before we notified you, we _____

_____

The school nurse _____

_____

I hope _____ feels better soon!

Sincerely,

_____   _____
Teacher   Date

Bump

CRUNCH

BANG

ouch!

------------------------------------ Cut here. ------------------------------------

Dear Parents:

Check Your Child for Lice

Lice are small grey-white insects that live and reproduce in the
scalp. They attach themselves to strands of hair and lay eggs.
When the eggs hatch, new insects begin to bite and irritate the
scalp. These bites cause itching, and if your child scratches, possible
infection.

It is certain that members of your child's class have been diagnosed with this. Here's what to
do if your child has head lice:

1. Find out if your child has an itchy scalp. If so, contact your physician for treatment.
2. Treat all family members at the same time, as they are often affected, too.
3. Disinfect bedding and clothing by machine washing in hot water. Clean combs and brushes
   thoroughly. Vacuum the carpet.

Your physician will give you professional treatment and alert you of any side effects. The
sooner you take care of this, the quicker it will get better.

Sincerely,

_____   _____
Teacher   Date

Your Child Is Sick!

Dear Parents:

_____
child

_____ looks feverish   _____ has a stomachache
_____ has fever   _____ has vomited
_____ is coughing and sneezing   _____ other: _____

_____
child

_____ needs to see a doctor
_____ needs rest
_____ must be kept away from the other children in class
_____ other: _____
       _____

Sincerely,

_____
Teacher

_____
Date

headache

earache

Sneezing

fever

coughing

bodyaches

stomachache

TLC10033 Copyright © Teaching & Learning Company, Carthage, IL 6232

Your Child Lost a Tooth!

Dear Parents:

It came out when _____ was

_____ .

Remember to have your child put it under the pillow tonight for a surprise tomorrow morning!

Sincerely,

_____
Teacher

_____
Date

-- Cut here. --

Cafeteria News!

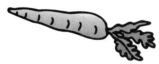

Dear Parents:

Want to know what's happening in the cafeteria?

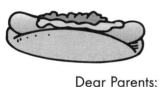

Here's the update: _____

_____

_____

_____

_____

Sincerely,

_____   _____
Teacher   Date

HAS BROKEN A CAFETERIA RULE

_____ Talking
_____ Running
_____ Throwing things
_____ Not cleaning up after oneself
_____ Other: _____

_____
Teacher

_____
Date

- Cut here. -

Has Great Cafeteria Manners!

_____ Enters orderly
_____ Cleans table properly
_____ Leaves orderly
_____ Helps keep the cafeteria clean
_____ Other: _____
_____
_____

_____   _____
Teacher   Date

TLC10033 Copyright © Teaching & Learning Company, Carthage, IL 623

Show & Tell

Dear Parent:

Show & Tell will be held

Day: _____

Date: _____

Time: _____

School: _____ **Room:** _____

Please stop by and hear what your child and other children have to say about the items they brought to share with the class. I feel sure that your presence will be a boost of encouragement.

Sincerely,

_____   _____
Teacher   Date

TLC10033 Copyright © Teaching & Learning Company, Carthage, IL 62321

Dear Parents:

A Field Trip

We're planning to go to _____

on _____. We're leaving at

and returning to school by _____.

This trip will enrich your child's education because

_____

Please have your child bring the following items:

1. _____

2. _____

3. _____

4. _____

_____   _____
Teacher   Date

------------------------------- Cut here. -------------------------------

_____ has my permission to

attend the field trip to _____ on

_____.

_____   _____
Parent   Date

TLC10033 Copyright © Teaching & Learning Company, Carthage, IL 62321

Dear Parents:

Read over these safety tips for the class field trip and discuss them with your child.

These rules are meant for the safety and protection of everyone involved. The field trip is to be enjoyed, and we need 100% cooperation. Please help!

1. Everyone is to stay with members of the class. Everyone goes to the same place. No wandering around.
2. Everyone is to remain seated while on the bus and not get up.
3. _____
   _____
4. _____
   _____
5. _____
   _____
6. _____
   _____
7. _____
   _____
8. _____
   _____

Sincerely,   SAFETY is No. 1

_____   _____
Teacher   Date

Dear Parents:

_____

has the opportunity to **bring home the class pet**

and needs your permission.

Our pet is a _____, and its name is _____.

We would like it to be your house guest

from _____ until _____.

It is a wonderful opportunity and experience for your child to take care of and learn to look after our class pet. It teaches responsibility and nurturing. Please consider it! Fill out the permission slip below and send it to school with your child by _____.

Sincerely,

_____   _____
Teacher   Date

--- Cut here. ---

_____ has my permission to bring home

the class pet on _____. We will return it

on _____.

_____   _____
Parent   Date

WANTED

A kind family
to care for me.
I need love
and attention.

TLC10033 Copyright © Teaching & Learning Company, Carthage, IL 6232

We Need Art Supplies

Dear Parents:

Our next art project is _____.
Please have your child bring in the items listed below.

_____

_____

_____

_____

_____

We need the supplies by _____.

Thank you for your help!

Sincerely,

_____   _____
Teacher   Date

TLC10033 Copyright © Teaching & Learning Company, Carthage, IL 62321

Chaperone Needed

Dear Parents:

Would you be interested in being a chaperone?

Event scheduled: _____

Date(s): _____

Time: _____

Place: _____

Please respond by _____

If you agree to chaperone, please fill in the information below.

Thanks!   Thank you!   Thanks!

Sincerely,

_____   _____

- - - - - - - - - - - - - - - - - - Cut here and return to school. - - - - - - - - - - - - - - - -

_____ Yes, I would be delighted to chaperone.

Event: _____

Name: _____

Daytime phone: _____ Evening phone: _____

- Cut here. -

Chaperone Confirmation Reminder

Thank you for agreeing to chaperone!

Please be at _____ **by** _____

                                   place   time

        on _____.

                            date

TLC10033 Copyright © Teaching & Learning Company, Carthage, IL 6232

Decorating Assistance

Dear Parents:

We are decorating and need your help. How about it? All about our plans: _____

_____

_____

_____

Where: _____

When: _____

Time: _____

Send me your answer by _____
If you agree to help decorate, please fill in the information below.

Thank you!

Sincerely,

_____   _____
Teacher   Date

- - - - - - - - - - - - - - - Cut here and return to school. - - - - - - - - - - - - - -

_____ Yes, I'd like to help decorate!

_____ Sorry, I can't be there.

Name: _____

Daytime phone: _____   Evening phone: _____

TLC10033 Copyright © Teaching & Learning Company, Carthage, IL 62321

Decorating Confirmation Reminder

Thank you for agreeing to decorate!

Please be at _____

place

by _____ on _____.

time   date

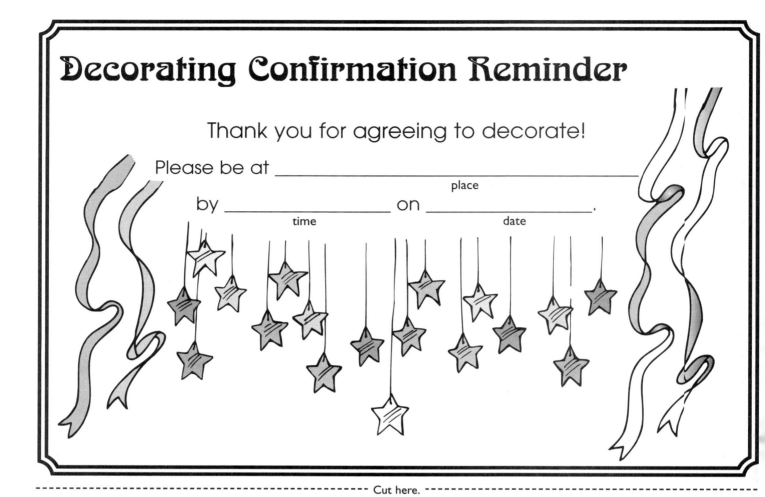

-------------------------------- Cut here. --------------------------------

WANTED: Food

Dear Parents:

We are planning _____.

Please have your child bring in the following foods:

1. _____
2. _____
3. _____
4. _____
5. _____

Send to school by_____.

Thanks! Your help is appreciated.

Sincerely,

_____

Teacher

_____

Date

TLC10033 Copyright © Teaching & Learning Company, Carthage, IL 62321

Homework Assistance, Please!

Dear Parents:

Your child needs help in _____.
subject

The problem is _____

_____

_____

You can help by _____

_____

_____

_____

If you have any questions regarding this note, please contact me
at ( ) _____,
during the hours

_____.

Sincerely,

_____

Teacher

_____

Date

TLC10033 Copyright © Teaching & Learning Company, Carthage, IL 62321

LUNCHROOM SUPERVISOR NEEDED

Dear Parents:

Your help is needed in the cafeteria to _____

_____.

You would be responsible for _____

_____.

Dates supervisor is needed are _____ from _____ to _____.

Sincerely,

_____   _____
Teacher   Date

------------------------------- Cut here and return to school. -------------------------------

_____ Yes, I would be happy to help out in the lunchroom.

Name: _____

Daytime phone: _____   Evening phone: _____

--- Cut here. ---

Lunchroom Supervisor Reminder

Thank you for agreeing to help in the lunchroom.

Please be in the school cafeteria.

_____
Time

Sincerely,

_____
Teacher

_____
Date

_____
Date

TLC10033 Copyright © Teaching & Learning Company, Carthage, IL 62

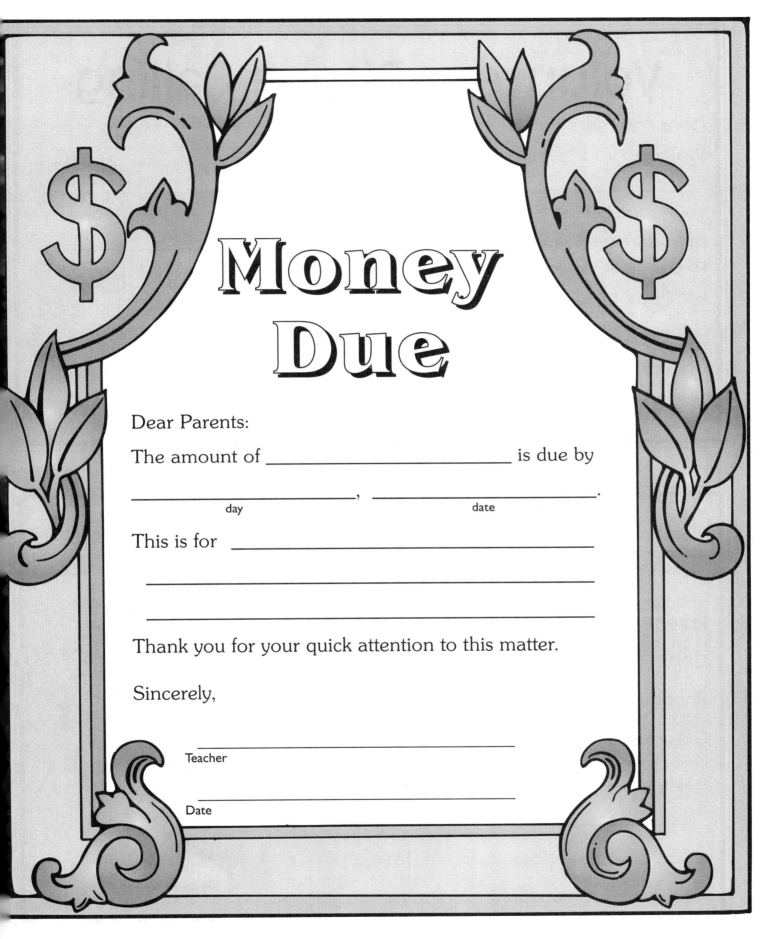

Money Due

Dear Parents:

The amount of _____ is due by

_____, _____.
day   date

This is for _____

_____

_____

Thank you for your quick attention to this matter.

Sincerely,

_____
Teacher

_____
Date

TLC10033 Copyright © Teaching & Learning Company, Carthage, IL 62321

Volunteer Phone Calling

Dear Parents:

We need your help making phone calls for _____

_____.

Your contribution of _____ calls would be a great help. They

need to be made by _____.

Please fill in the information below and send it to school

with your child if you can help.

Thank you!

Sincerely,

_____   _____
Teacher   Date

---------------------------- Cut here and return to school. ----------------------------

_____ Yes, I can make calls!

Parents: _____

Child: _____

Phone number: _____

Comments: _____

_____

_____

_____

TLC10033 Copyright © Teaching & Learning Company, Carthage, IL 62321

Phone Call Confirmation

To: _____

Thank you for agreeing to make calls for _____

_____.

Details to relate: _____

_____

_____

Here's a list of names and numbers.

Name   **Number**

_____   _____

_____   _____

_____   _____

_____   _____

_____   _____

_____   _____

Comments: _____

_____

_____

A Call for Recyclable Materials

Dear Parents:

We need your throwaway items for _____

_____.

Please have your child bring in the following cleaned items:

_____ glass bottles   _____ empty coffee cans

_____ glass jars   _____ empty cereal boxes

_____ aluminum cans   _____ old newspapers

_____ aluminum foil   _____ empty shoe boxes

_____ plastic bags   _____ scrap paper

_____ old toys   _____ old socks

_____ old books   _____

_____ old clothes   _____

_____ egg cartons   _____

_____ paper towel rolls   _____

_____ toilet paper rolls   Other: _____

_____ empty milk cartons   _____

In our class, we are committed to making a difference in the world by recycling old materials and reusing them. Thank you for helping us achieve this goal!

Sincerely,

_____   _____
Teacher   Date

TLC10033 Copyright © Teaching & Learning Company, Carthage, IL 62321

A Call for School Supplies

Dear Parents:

We need your throwaway items for _____

_____

Please have your child bring in the following items:

_____   _____

_____   _____

_____   _____

_____   _____

_____   _____

_____   _____

Due by _____

Thank you for your generous help.

Sincerely,

_____   _____
Teacher   Date

TLC10033 Copyright © Teaching & Learning Company, Carthage, IL 62321

Special Events Coordinator

Dear Parents:

Are you interested in helping coordinate _____

_____?

The job would entail _____

_____

_____

The event will take place . . .

Date: _____

Time: _____

Place: _____

Please fill in the information below and send it to school with your child if you are willing to take on this job.

Thank you!

Sincerely,

_____   _____
Teacher   Date

-------------------------------- Cut here and return to school. --------------------------------

_____ Yes, I can help coordinate the _____

_____

Parents: _____   Child: _____

Phone number: _____

Comments: _____

_____

TLC10033 Copyright © Teaching & Learning Company, Carthage, IL 62321

Special Events Coordinator

Confirmation

To: _____

Thank you for agreeing to help coordinate _____
_____.

Here's a list of things that need taking care of.

_____
_____
_____
_____
_____
_____
_____
_____

TLC10033 Copyright © Teaching & Learning Company, Carthage, IL 62321

A CALL FOR SMALL EQUIPMENT

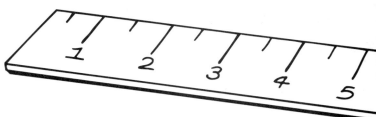

Dear Parents:

We need small equipment for

_____.

Can you help us locate or bring in the following items:

1. _____
2. _____
3. _____

Due by _____.

Thank you for helping us out!

Sincerely,

_____   _____
Teacher   Date

TLC10033 Copyright © Teaching & Learning Company, Carthage, IL 62321

Speaker Wanted

Dear Parents:

We are looking for parents who want to come to our classroom and talk about their jobs. This would give us the chance to get to know you, as well as allow the class the opportunity to explore and learn about your field of expertise. We are looking for parents excited about their careers, their volunteer work and their work in the home. Please take time to fill out the form below and return it to school with your child by_____.

Sincerely,

_____   _____
Teacher   Date

- Cut here and return to school. -

Parents: _____   Child: _____

_____ Yes, I would like to come speak to the class about my job!

_____ No, I will pass on speaking right now.

My job title is _____.

My responsibilities include _____

_____.

_____.

Best days to come speak are _____.

Best times to come speak are _____.

TLC10033 Copyright © Teaching & Learning Company, Carthage, IL 62321

Speaker Confirmation

To: _____

Thank you for agreeing to speak about being a _____

_____.

You are scheduled for . . .

Day: _____

Date: _____

Time: _____

Contact me only if this doesn't work with your schedule.

Sincerely,

_____   _____
Teacher   Date

Today's Visiting
Speaker
Mr. Pott's
POTT'S PETS

TLC10033 Copyright © Teaching & Learning Company, Carthage, IL 62321

 # Cultural Speaker Wanted

Dear Parents:

We are looking for parents who want to come to our classroom and talk about their cultural background. This would give us the chance to get to know you, as well as allow the class the opportunity to learn all about your cultural heritage. We want to know about your customs, your way of life, the foods you grew up with and how things are different and similar to your life here.

Please take time to fill out the form below and return it to school with your child by _____.

Sincerely,

_____   _____
Teacher   Date

--------------------------------- Cut here and return to school. --------------------------------

Parents: _____   Child: _____

_____ Yes, I would like to come speak to the class about my
cultural heritage!

_____ No, I will pass on speaking right now.

My cultural background is _____.

Comments: _____

_____

_____

Best days to come speak are _____.

Best times to come speak are _____.

Cultural Speaker Confirmation

To: _____

Thank you for agreeing to speak about your native culture, _____

_____.

You are scheduled for . . .

Day: _____

Date: _____

Time: _____

Contact me only if this doesn't work with your schedule.

Sincerely,

_____   _____
Teacher   Date

TLC10033 Copyright © Teaching & Learning Company, Carthage, IL 6232

Storyteller Wanted

Dear Parents:

Do you tell stories to your child or children? Would you be willing to tell these same stories or different ones to your child's class?

Storytelling is a wonderful way of passing on values to young children. It is also an intimate form of classroom entertainment. Aside from these reasons, storytelling is just plain fun, and we enjoy storytelling time in our class.

Please consider coming to our class and telling stories during story hour. Fill out the form below and return it to school with your child by _____.

Sincerely,

_____   _____
Teacher   Date

-------------------------------- Cut here and return to school. --------------------------------

Parents: _____   Child: _____

_____ Yes, I would like to come speak to class and tell stories!

_____ No, I will pass on storytelling right now.

_____ I plan to tell stories.

_____ I plan to read stories aloud.

_____ I plan to do both.

Comments: _____

_____

_____.

Best days to come to class are _____.

Best times to come to class are _____.

Storyteller Confirmation

To: _____

Thank you for agreeing to tell stories to the class. We are excited about the event. _____

_____

You are scheduled for . . .

Day: _____

Date: _____

Time: _____

Contact me only if this doesn't work with your schedule.

Sincerely,

_____   _____
Teacher   Date

TLC10033 Copyright © Teaching & Learning Company, Carthage, IL 6232

VOLUNTEER *Assistance*

Dear Parents:

Can you help? We need volunteers for _____

_____.

Please fill in the information below and send it to school with your child if you can volunteer.

Thank you!

Sincerely,

_____   _____
Teacher   Date

- Cut here and return to school. - - - - - - - - - - - - - - - - - - -

Parents: _____   Child: _____

_____ Yes, I can volunteer.

_____ No, I cannot volunteer at this time.

VOLUNTEER

Phone number: _____

Comments: _____

_____

_____

- Cut here. -

Volunteer Confirmation

To: _____

Thank you for agreeing to volunteer for _____

_____.

Comments: _____

_____

_____

Sincerely,

_____   _____
Teacher   Date

We Need . . .

Dear Parents:

Can you help? We need _____

_____.

This will be used for _____

_____

_____.

Date due: _____

Thank you for your support and generosity!

Sincerely,

_____   _____
Teacher   Date

TLC10033 Copyright © Teaching & Learning Company, Carthage, IL 6232

Come to a Back-to-School Night

This is our opportunity to meet one another and talk about what we're doing in school.
Come by so that I can tell you all about our daily plans, our upcoming projects and show you
what we've been working on this year.
I look forward to seeing you!

_____
teacher

School: _____

Room: _____

Date: _____

Time: _____

- Cut here. - - - - - - - - - - - - - - - - - - -

Parents, fill out this form and return it to me with your child.

Parents:_____

_____ Yes, I will attend Back-to-School Night.

_____ No, I will not be able to make it.

Please write your questions or comments below.

_____

_____

_____

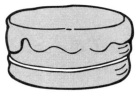

You Are Invited to a Bake Sale

Baked goods will be on sale to help raise money for __
_____.

We need your support. Please come by

School: _____

Room: _____

Date:_____

Time: _____

-------------------------------- Cut here. ---------------------------------

Send this form back to school with your child.

_____ Yes, I can help at the bake sale.

_____ No, I will not be able to assist.

_____   _____
Name   Phone number

I can help: (Mark one or more!)

_____ plan   _____ organize   _____ set up

_____ volunteer   _____ spread the word   _____ bake

_____ other:_____

118

TLC10033 Copyright © Teaching & Learning Company, Carthage, IL 6232

The School Book Fair Is for You, Too!

The School Book Fair is here! Please join your child at this exciting event! Watch how excited kids get about reading! You'll be excited, too!

Come look around, browse and shop in a relaxed no-pressure atmosphere. There's a book for every young reader at every price.

Stop by and see for yourself!

Place: _____

Room: _____

Date: _____

Hours: _____

Cut here.

A Carnival!

Join us for a festive affair!

Games!   *Prizes!*   *Food!*   *Fun!*

When: _____

Where: _____

What time: _____

Be there!

LC10033 Copyright © Teaching & Learning Company, Carthage, IL 62321

A Celebration!

We are planning a special event in our classroom on _____ at

_____
time

The event is _____ .

It would be great if you could be there with us.

Sincerely,

_____   _____
Teacher   Date

-- Cut here. --

To: _____

A reminder that the class is holding a special event soon.

Date: _____   Time: _____

Please plan to attend.

-- Cut here. --

Please return this note to school with your child.

Parents: _____

_____ *Yes, I am looking forward to being at the class celebration.*

_____ *No, I will not be able to make the big event.*

TLC10033 Copyright © Teaching & Learning Company, Carthage, IL 6232

Come to a _____ Club Event

The event promises to _____
_____.

We look forward to seeing you there!

Place: _____

Room: _____

Date: _____

Time: _____

-------------------------------- Cut here. --------------------------------

Come to a Concert

And what a musical performance it will be!

Who's performing: _____

About the program: _____

_____

Where: _____

When: _____

What time: _____

C10033 Copyright © Teaching & Learning Company, Carthage, IL 62321

Come to a Parent/Teacher Conference

It's scheduled for _____ at
_____ o'clock.

Write down the things you want to discuss and bring in this sheet with you.

_____

_____

_____

_____

_____

_____

- Cut here. -

Come to a Demonstration
and See for Yourself

What is being explained: _____

_____

What you will get out of it:_____

_____

Place: _____

Date: _____

Time: _____

See you there!

TLC10033 Copyright © Teaching & Learning Company, Carthage, IL 6232

Family Fun Night

This is what we're planning: _____

_____

_____

_____ .

*It's going to be a great evening.
Sure hope you'll be there to share the fun!*

Place: _____

Date: _____

Time: _____

Welcome to FamilyNight

- Cut here. -

Field Day Is Coming Up!

The biggest track and field event ever! Be there!

Come watch _____

take part in _____ .

Field Day is scheduled for _____ .

Place: _____

Time: _____

Attend Our Fund-Raiser

Money is being raised for_____

_____.

Plans for the fund-raiser include _____

_____

_____.

You can help by_____

_____

_____.

Please complete the bottom half of this form and return it
to me with your child as soon as possible.

Sincerely,

_____   _____
Teacher   Date

- Cut here. -

We'd love to have you help, whether you can attend or not.

_____ Yes, I plan to attend the fund-raiser.

_____ No, I will not be able to attend.

Parents: _____   Child: _____

Date: _____

TLC10033 Copyright © Teaching & Learning Company, Carthage, IL 62321

An Event for Grandparents

A special bill of fare for grandparents!

Please come to our class for _____

_____.

School: _____

Date: _____ Time: _____

Comments: _____

_____

_____

This will be a very special day.
We hope you'll be a part of it all!

Fill in and return to school with your grandchild.

-------------------------------- Cut here. --------------------------------

I'm/We're _____ 's

____ grandma

____ grandpa

____ grandparents

____ I/We plan to attend the special day
for grandparents!

____ Sorry, I/we can't come to the
special day for grandparents.

Grandpa with me on Grandparents' Day!

Come to a Holiday Party

Join the festivities!
We're going to have a blast!

Theme: _____

Place: _____

Date: _____

Time: _____

Please bring _____.

Comments: _____

_____

Don't miss it!

- Cut here. -

COME TO AN
OPEN HOUSE

Location: _____

Date: _____

Time: _____

I look forward to seeing you there!

_____

Teacher

_____

Date

TLC10033 Copyright © Teaching & Learning Company, Carthage, IL 62321

A Parade
Come hear the music.

Reason for the event: _____

_____

Starting place: _____

Ending place: _____

Date: _____

Time: _____

It's going to be quite a display.

---------------------------------- Cut here. ----------------------------------

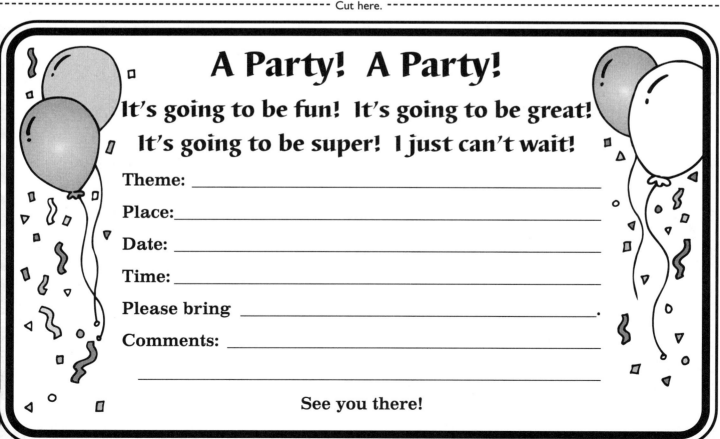

A Party! A Party!

It's going to be fun! It's going to be great!
It's going to be super! I just can't wait!

Theme: _____

Place: _____

Date: _____

Time: _____

Please bring _____.

Comments: _____

_____

See you there!

TLC10033 Copyright © Teaching & Learning Company, Carthage, IL 62321

You're Invited to a Play

Please join us.

Title of play: _____

Being performed by _____

Location: _____

Date: _____

Time: _____

-------------------------------- Cut here. --------------------------------

PTA GOALS

Come to a PTA Meeting

We need your support!

On the agenda _____

_____

Where: _____

When: _____

Time: _____

*Thank you for taking an active part
in your child's schooling.*

TLC10033 Copyright © Teaching & Learning Company, Carthage, IL 62321

A Recital!

Come hear the music.

Program: _____

Presented by _____

Place: _____

Date: _____

Time: _____

-- Cut here. --

SCIENCE FAIR

Attend the Science Fair

Great projects!

Highly entertaining and informative!

Taking place from _____ to _____

in the _____

_____.

Hours open: _____

You are invited to hear a speaker!

_____

will be speaking on the subject of

_____

Location: _____

Date: _____

Time: _____

Post this note as a reminder.

------------------------------------- Cut here. -------------------------------------

Come to a Sports Event

Fun • Excitement • Competition • Diversion

What's taking place: _____

Who's participating: _____

Place: _____

Date: _____

Time: _____

TLC10033 Copyright © Teaching & Learning Company, Carthage, IL 62321

Come Listen to a Story

During Story Hour and Hear a Wonderful Tale Unfold

Story being told: _____

Storyteller: _____

Place: _____

Date: _____

Time: _____

-- Cut here. --

Support Group Meeting

For _____
_____

Location: _____

Date: _____   Time: _____

Post this note as your reminder.

A Talent Show

Sit back, relax and be entertained!

Performers: _____

Place: _____

Date: _____

Time: _____

This promises to be special!

An Assembly Is Being Planned

to go over _____

with _____.

Please plan to attend.

Where: _____

When: _____

From: _____ to _____

Post this notice as a reminder.

Cut here.

TLC10033 Copyright © Teaching & Learning Company, Carthage, IL 62321

You Are Invited to a

_____

Hope to see you there!

Place: _____

Date: _____

Time: _____

Post this note as a reminder.

------------------------------- Cut here. -------------------------------

You Are Invited to a

_____

Hope to see you there!

Place: _____

Date: _____

Time: _____

Post this note as a reminder.

WELCOME

Welcome to School, _____.
student's name

I am looking forward to having you in my class this year!

My name is _____.
teacher's name

--- Cut here. ---

Welcome to Our School,

_____.

I am looking forward to having you in my class this year.

If you have any questions, please ask me.

I have asked _____ to show you around until _____.

My name is _____.
teacher's name

--- Cut here. ---

_____
student's name

Please show the new student, _____,

around the school until _____.

TLC10033 Copyright © Teaching & Learning Company, Carthage, IL 62321

You Are Appreciated!

To: _____

You are appreciated because _____

_____.

We admire who you are and what
you stand for.

Thank you for everything.

We are truly grateful.

From:_____

_____

Cut here.

BIG NEWS!

Did you hear about it?

_____

_____

_____

_____

_____

_____

How do you like that information?

TLC10033 Copyright © Teaching & Learning Company, Carthage, IL 62321

Congratulations!

To: _____

This is just to say that we couldn't be happier for you.

Keep up the good work.

From: _____

-------------------------------- Cut here. -------------------------------------

Get Well Soon!

To: _____

We heard you're sick.

From all your friends in class _____

and _____.

 teacher

TLC10033 Copyright © Teaching & Learning Company, Carthage, IL 62321

There's going to be a
Giant
Celebration,
and you're invited!

Please come and be a part of it all!

We're celebrating _____

_____

Where: _____

When: _____

Cut here.

To: _____

Good Job!
You did excellent work!
Keep it up!
I'm very proud of you.

_____
teacher

Happy Birthday,

_____

You're _____ years old!

Have a very happy birthday and lots of fun today!

From: _____

teacher

- Cut here. -

To: _____

This is a note to say . . .

_____

_____

_____

_____

_____

_____

_____

From: _____

TLC10033 Copyright © Teaching & Learning Company, Carthage, IL 62321

To: _____

You should be very proud because

you _____ !

We are all very pleased for you.

From your classmates in room

_____ and _____

teacher

Great Job!

---------------------------- Cut here. ----------------------------

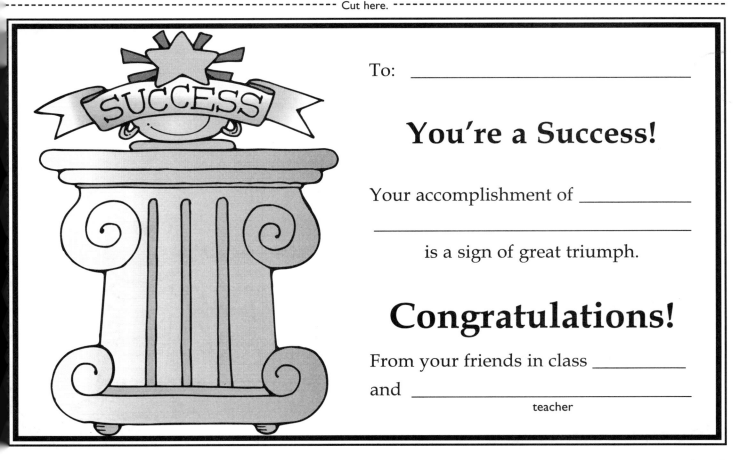

To: _____

You're a Success!

Your accomplishment of _____

_____

is a sign of great triumph.

Congratulations!

From your friends in class _____

and _____

teacher

SUCCESS

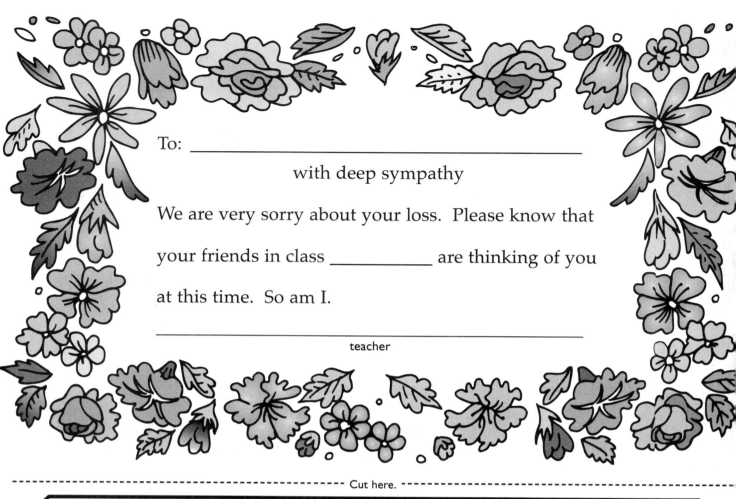

To: _____

with deep sympathy

We are very sorry about your loss. Please know that

your friends in class _____ are thinking of you

at this time. So am I.

_____
teacher

- Cut here. -

To: _____

You showed teamwork with

_____

when you joined together and got the job done.

I applaud you.

_____
teacher

TLC10033 Copyright © Teaching & Learning Company, Carthage, IL 62321

To: _____

Thank You!

I appreciate your thoughtfulness of

_____

You are very nice.

From: _____

teacher

----------------------------- Cut here. -----------------------------

To: _____

You Are Special

because _____

_____

_____

From: _____

teacher

TLC10033 Copyright © Teaching & Learning Company, Carthage, IL 62321

TO: _____

WE'RE SORRY TO HEAR

_____

_____

ALL OUR BEST

FROM YOUR FRIENDS IN CLASS _____ AND

_____ .

teacher

---------------------------- Cut here. ----------------------------

TO: _____

While you were gone, you missed

_____

_____

_____

_____

_____

From: _____

teacher

TLC10033 Copyright © Teaching & Learning Company, Carthage, IL 62321

* Part 2 *
Communication for
Report Cards and Assessments

In this section, there are more than 175 model notes for briefly conveying anything and everything you need to say to a parent about their child's behavioral or academic performance during the grading period. Use these notes word-for-word, or as suggestions for adapting to your particular needs and requirements.

For effective communication, you will want to copy these messages in your own handwriting directly onto a child's report card, or on personal or school stationery.

You will find simple ways to praise a child and smooth ways to inspire while reprimanding. You will find short, general notes in every subject area for let-

ting a parent know exactly how the child is doing in arithmetic, language arts or social studies. You will find generic ways of commenting regarding a child's abilities in the classroom. Most notes in this section are arranged in an easy-to-use alphabetical format. You will find the positive comments on pages 144-153. Comments of concern are on pages 154-167 and curriculum areas begin on page 168. Encouragements are on pages 184-189.

Remember that these notes are standards. Use this section as a guide during the critically important times of report card grading and assessments.

Bright	Cheery	Confident	Cooperative

_____

is a very bright child. He is clever, talented and quick-witted. He has

special talent in _____

and shows leadership ability in this area.

_____'s

mood and disposition are always cheery.

She is easy to be around because her good spirits and pleasant

outlook affect others with enthusiasm.

_____'s

sense of confidence comes across as strong and positive. His

self-reliance and independence, especially in the area of

_____, allow him to

get the job done in a timely and effective manner.

_____

is always willing to cooperate. She is a team player who has an exceptional ability to

work together for a common goal. Because of

her strength in participating,

work is done in record time.

TLC10033 Copyright © Teaching & Learning Company, Carthage, IL 62321

Creative	Delightful	Eager	Enthusiastic

_____'s

creativity in _____ is both

inventive and imaginative. His work is original, and he seldom lacks

for inspiration. Continue to nurture his love and ability in this area!

_____

is delightful and a pleasure to be around.
Her charming personality and joyful demeanor
make her well-liked by classmates.
It's been wonderful having her as a student.

_____

is eager to

_____.

His energetic approach is a wonderful quality, and he's
an excessively diligent student.

_____

has a delightful enthusiasm for _____.

Her strong interest in the area makes her a natural for
doing such a great job. With her amount of zest and pas-
sion, I will continue to support and nurture her work.

_____ is friendly and well-liked by classmates. He is giving of himself and is approachable. His openness and willingness to help others seem prompted by kindness.

_____ is fun, lively and playful! She enjoys having a good time and has the ability to make others see the gaiety in things, whether routine or amusement. It is delightful to be around her.

_____ has good manners. He is polite and shows grace in his style of _____. His conduct in this area is quite admirable. It is nice to spend time with him.

_____ is a happy and contented child. She smiles often and is satisfied with whatever is going on at the time. She has an easy-going manner, and it is effortless to be around her.

TLC10033 Copyright © Teaching & Learning Company, Carthage, IL 6232

_____
is a helpful child. He is always willing to assist and provide support when needed. He makes himself useful around the classroom and always makes a valuable contribution to school.

_____
is highly imaginative when it comes to
_____. Her
resourcefulness is inspiring to everyone she's around.
May this gift of originality be with her for a long time to come.

_____ actively involves himself, especially in
_____.
He participates in this wholeheartedly and concerns himself as fully as possible. He takes great pride in seeing the activity through from beginning to end.

_____
is an intelligent child. She understands the material covered in class and knows how to incorporate it.
She has a quick mind and a high level of capability.

LC10033 Copyright © Teaching & Learning Company, Carthage, IL 62321

_____

is kind and has a gentle nature. He shows affection and consideration to those he comes in contact with.
It is a pleasure having him as part of the class.

_____

is a natural-born leader. Her classmates find her easy to follow because of her ability to guide them in the right direction and because of the influential person she is.

_____

is a loving and affectionate child. His classmates are fond of being around him, and he shows a great liking and trust to those he comes in contact with.
He brightens our lives each and every day.

_____

_____ is neat in
_____. This area of her work is always tidy and uncluttered. She is an orderly child, and the quality of being neat is a good habit to have during the school years and for the rest of her life.

148

TLC10033 Copyright © Teaching & Learning Company, Carthage, IL 6232

 is one of the nicest people. His pleasant attitude makes it easy to be around him. He is warm and polite and popular among peers, who naturally gravitate to spending time with him.

is organized and systematic. Her work is orderly and arranged well. I can always count on receiving a tidy paper from her when work is due.

participates well and takes a large role in _____.

 In this area of school, he is especially interested and does a super job. Once he puts his mind to a task, he usually does it well.

is a child that can be relied upon. She is of sound and consistent character which makes it easy to depend on her. She is honest and trusted among friends.

_____ is resourceful enough to get what he wants and needs in life. He uses his abilities and quick-wittedness for anything that may eventually help him further his education and future plans.

_____ is poised and self-confident. She is sure of herself, yet not conceited or overly confident. The assignments she undertakes get done in timely and efficient manner because she is sure of her abilities.

_____ is a self-starter who needs no extra motivation. He takes on schoolwork in a serious manner and is ready to tackle almost anything put before him. _____'s ambitious nature is a fine quality.

_____ is a sensible child. She shows good common sense and seems to know what to do in most situations. Other students look to her for her rational and practical approach to solving an issue.

TLC10033 Copyright © Teaching & Learning Company, Carthage, IL 6232

| Sociable | Sweet | Talented | Thoughtful |

_____

 is a a sociable child who likes the company of many acquaintances. He is warm and outgoing and easy for others to include as a friend. He takes the idea of friendship seriously.

_____

has a sweet disposition and a gentle temperament. She is always pleasant to be around and rarely fusses. She brings a freshness to the classroom and makes it a nice place to be.

_____

has a real talent for _____.

 With this special flair, he has the ability to go far in this area. I suggest it be nurtured so that his aptitude improves over time.

_____

is a thoughtful and considerate child. She is mindful of the feelings of others and is careful to always say the right thing. Her compassionate nature makes her well-liked by many.

LC10033 Copyright © Teaching & Learning Company, Carthage, IL 62321

_____

is a tireless and energetic child. He is spirited and seems to have inexhaustible energy. Whatever he puts his mind to, it is done in an unfaltering and dynamic manner.

_____

is a trustworthy child. Whatever she says she will do, it gets done because of her reliability. She exceeds all expectations in this area.

is versatile, adaptable and capable of dealing with many projects. She can turn easily from one to another. This is an excellent and multifaceted quality which allows for a great amount of flexibility in life.

_____

is a well-adjusted child who is capable of anything. She makes herself familiar with any new situation and goes into most anything with a positive outlook. This is a winning quality, which makes her a delight to work with.

TLC10033 Copyright © Teaching & Learning Company, Carthage, IL 6232

_____

is well-liked. He has many close friends who trust and feel secure around him.
His easygoing and assured personality is attractive to those
who meet him and comforting to those who
look for a lasting friendship.

_____

is wise and prudent. She exhibits reasonable behavior day
after day and is inspiring to be around. She is available to
inform others when necessary and does so in a bright
and sensible manner.

_____

is a zany and playful child. He is frolicsome and often keeps the
other children laughing. His quick wit and merrymaking make
him a pleasure to have in class.

_____

has a zest for life. She has a keen interest and enjoyment in
so many areas, and this aspect of her personality makes her
delightful to be around. Spending time with her, it is
easy to pick up her gusto!

.C10033 Copyright © Teaching & Learning Company, Carthage, IL 62321

_____

is often absent from class and must come more frequently if her grades are to improve. She shows promise in the area of _____ but needs to be in school for lessons in _____. Please alert your child of the importance to attend class on a regular basis.

has a largely aggressive nature. He is forceful towards other classmates, which makes many children uncomfortable being around him. Although it is good that he can never be bullied, he needs to cool down his too-assertive behavior.

_____'s

attitude toward school needs to change. Her way of thinking is negative, and she refuses to work with the administration in coming up with a plan that will be suitable for her. Can you help in making an adjustment in her attitude?

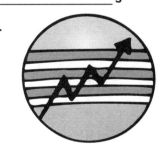

_____

has bad manners when it comes to _____.
With a bit of coaching and disciplining during school time, I think he could vastly improve this behavior. Good manners are something to be taught and practiced—both at home and during school.

TLC10033 Copyright © Teaching & Learning Company, Carthage, IL 6232

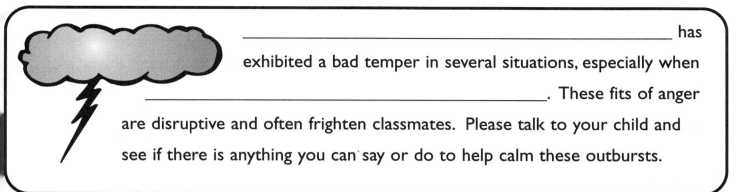

_____ has exhibited a bad temper in several situations, especially when _____. These fits of anger are disruptive and often frighten classmates. Please talk to your child and see if there is anything you can say or do to help calm these outbursts.

_____ has a problem biting. This act is harmful and immature. If your child needs attention, there are other ways to get it; ways that will affect him and his classmates in a positive manner. Let's work on this together so that we can replace this action with a worthwhile quality.

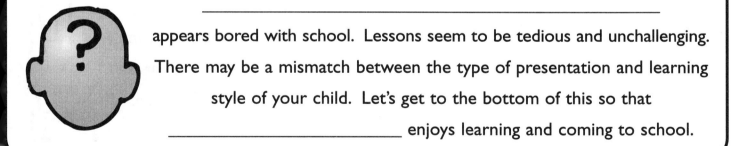

_____ appears bored with school. Lessons seem to be tedious and unchallenging. There may be a mismatch between the type of presentation and learning style of your child. Let's get to the bottom of this so that _____ enjoys learning and coming to school.

_____ has been breaking rules lately, especially the ones concerning _____. This must stop so that the standard way of doing things can get back to normal. Please talk to your child and explain that he is required to conform to school rules while he is here.

_____

is often seen bullying other classmates. She pushes around those who

_____. There are

many wonderful qualities about your child, and it would be to everyone's

benefit if those were brought out more often and the bullying stopped.

_____

was caught cheating on _____. This behavior is

unacceptable. Please talk to your child about why he feels the need to

cheat. We must correct the underlying problem so that your child can

go on to work in an acceptable manner in which he is very capable.

_____

chews gum during class, which is not allowed. Not only is the gum chewing

and popping bothersome, it is also messy if not disposed of properly. Please

ask your child to leave the gum at home—or in her pocket—from now on.

_____

often complains about _____. His moaning and

groaning in this area are getting old; there must be

something else constructive to take its place. If you can find the root of the complaints,

I would be most appreciative if you would share this information with me.

TLC10033 Copyright © Teaching & Learning Company, Carthage, IL 62321

_____'s
ability to concentrate could be better developed. She has a difficult time
focusing her attention on her lessons. If she were to
simply apply herself, she could do a good job
because she is a capable person.

_____

has been unwilling to cooperate lately. He does not seem to want
to work together or participate in group activities, which is a vital
part of learning. He is capable of contributing a great deal
but must be motivated in this direction.

_____ was spotted copying.
This is unacceptable in my classroom and punishable by
_____. Please address this issue with
your child in order that she is discouraged from doing this again.
She is bright and doesn't need to copy to get the right answers.

_____

has damaged school property in the amount of $_____. This must be repaid
by cash or _____ by the date of
_____. Please discuss this with your child and get back to me on
how payment will be made. We are sorry to have to alert you about this incident.

TLC10033 Copyright © Teaching & Learning Company, Carthage, IL 62321

_____

is often found daydreaming. Although daydreaming can be quite imaginative, it is disrupting your child's learning abilities. Her attention is often on other things besides schoolwork. She is slow to react and blocks out class lessons.

_____ has disobeyed and

broken rules. Because of this, he must face the consequence of _____.

Should he ignore the rules again, the following punishment will be enforced:

_____.

Please discuss the consequences of disregarding rules with your child.

_____

is disorganized in her schoolwork. She seems to have no orderly system of classifying and organizing. Her work is confusing and messy. If she could come up with a simple system, her schoolwork and grades should improve, as well as her self-confidence.

_____

is disrespectful of _____ in the following

way: _____.

This is impolite and your child knows better than this. Please talk to your child and tell him the value and importance of respecting others and their belongings.

TLC10033 Copyright © Teaching & Learning Company, Carthage, IL 62321

_____

is disruptive and often disturbs the class. If she puts her mind more to her studies and less to interfering, she would do much better work. Please talk to her about her behavior, so that she can become a better all-around student.

_____

is often distracted from schoolwork; his attention is elsewhere. If he were to put his mind to his lessons, he would get much more out of school. Please discuss this with your child and see if you can come up with a solution that will help interest him in his work.

_____ is failing the subject of

_____ .

_____ She's not trying, so that she can fail.
_____ She's not doing homework unless she gets it all right.
_____ Other: _____

Let's do what we can to get her on the right track again.

_____

has a difficult time following directions. He does not take well to instruction or supervision. During individual projects and play, he does an excellent job, but when he is made to follow directions, he is less likely to be happy.

_____ does not fol-
low rules well. She is often caught doing what she is told not to do. Poor
behavior is punished by _____ .
Please discuss the consequences of breaking rules so that your child can
participate more fully in all class activities.

_____
has a habit of forgetting to bring in his homework lately. He is a
good student, but without turning in homework assignments, he
cannot make the grades he deserves. Please talk to your child
about the importance of turning in homework on its due date.

_____
was found hitting _____ .
This act is hurtful and unnecessary. Explain to your child that there are
other ways of handling anger besides hitting someone so that something
positive, rather than harmful, can come from a quarrel.

_____
is an impatient person at times. He gets uneasy and agitated
when _____ .
Let's discuss with him how the virtue of waiting
and how being patient can be a fine quality to develop.

TLC10033 Copyright © Teaching & Learning Company, Carthage, IL 62321

_____ has been turning

in incomplete work. The problem may be that she:

_____ doesn't understand the assignment

_____ is not self-motivated or self-confident about work

_____ has a problem in another area that is spilling into this area

Please call so that we can discuss this further.

_____

has a habit of interrupting others when they are speaking.
Talking out of turn is impolite and it must stop. Please tell your
child how important it is to let everyone have their turn talking.
Once he begins listening, he will find how interesting people can be.

_____

is irresponsible when it comes to _____.

She acts careless and unreliable in this area; however in

other areas of school life, she shows great responsibility, so

I know she is capable of fully exercising this trait.

_____

was found kicking _____ today. Although she may be
annoyed with or not like this person, it is important to remember that we must
handle differences by talking and understanding each other better. Please go
over the importance of talking and listening and why physical harm is not good
for any party.

TLC10033 Copyright © Teaching & Learning Company, Carthage, IL 62321

has a know-it-all attitude. She seems ready to express her knowledge to anyone and everyone—no matter if it is right or wrong. A bit more modesty in this area is advised.

brings in homework assignments late. He must understand the concept of time and get into the habit of handing in assignments when they are due, no matter if they are completed or not. This is important training for other areas in life.

has trouble listening to people when they are talking. She interrupts and makes no effort to hear what the other person is saying. She needs to learn to give her attention to whomever has the floor. Please discuss the merits of being a good listener with your child.

has been found lying about _____. It is a serious offense to invent a story in the place of the truth or to get out of a situation by being untruthful. It is important to remedy this issue so that your child knows that the truth is always better than a lie.

TLC10033 Copyright © Teaching & Learning Company, Carthage, IL 62321

_____

has been misbehaving and was reprimanded for behaving in a disorderly fashion today. Please let your child know that mis- conduct in the classroom is punishable by _____. Let's both remind her that she can get the things she wants most by acting properly.

_____'s

_____ assignments have been missing, and
subject

he attributes it to _____. Our next

assignment is due _____.

Please see that he has it on my desk on time.

Don't Forget!

_____   _____

often calls his peers unflattering names. This creates a feeling of resentment toward your child, and it has other serious consequences such as causing hurt to another child. Please ask your child to refrain from name-calling, and help him deal with the actual event that is causing pain.

_____   _____

is nonconforming when it comes to _____.

Being an individual is certainly a virtue, however, being a radical when it comes to the area described is just acting rebellious. Please assist your child in seeing that it is best to conform to some necessary things during school time.

_____

was found passing notes to her classmates during

_____. Although this is not a crime, it is

disruptive during class. Your child may be popular, however there are many

other times to communicate with friends outside the lesson.

_____

is often not paying attention. It seems that he has trouble

concentrating. He cannot focus his attention on the day's

lesson. Please contact me in order to help me ,understand what I can do to

arouse his attention so that school can be a positive experience for him.

_____

is influenced by peer pressure and acts out by

_____.

If she were more confident in who she is and less concerned with what others think,

she would be more productive.

_____

uses poor language and dirty words around his classmates. This is unac-

ceptable behavior in my class and something of which I disapprove. Please

discuss the use of words with your child so that his language and

vocabulary are fit for everyone around him to hear.

TLC10033 Copyright © Teaching & Learning Company, Carthage, IL 62321

_____,
from what I gather, has poor study habits. She is not an independent learner because she has not been taught to study properly. If you would like suggestions on getting your child into good study habits, please contact me.

_____
has a difficult time relating with other classmates. Your child is bright but often does not connect with children his own age. Possibly it is a case of shyness; possibly he is awkward socially. I will do all that I can to help him during school time.

_____
does not give consideration or respect to others. She insults and interrupts often. This is unacceptable behavior and something that must be dealt with. I am working on getting her to acknowledge that being respectful of others is a positive habit

_____'s
self-esteem is low. He does not believe in himself or his abilities, even though he is highly capable of performing at a greater degree than he does. He is competent and has the ability of much more than he thinks!

_____

was caught stealing from _____.

This act is punishable by _____. Please help

your child understand that taking someone's property without asking is a

form of theft and that anything she wants can be obtained by working or asking for it.

often talks in class out of turn. It is disruptive to me and to the

other students and makes learning difficult. Please discuss with

your child the merits of listening to others and why it's not

acceptable to talk whenever he feels like talking.

_____

is tardy to class and often runs behind schedule. Because of the

lateness, she will have to _____.

Please go over why being punctual to class is an excellent

habit to get into and do help her get into this routine.

_____ is often seen as a tattletale

by his classmates. He gossips idly and talks to friends about things that are often better

unsaid. Although I appreciate knowing of any disruptive or

harmful behavior, I want your child to be liked by his peers,

and I'm afraid too much tattling will harm his relationships.

TLC10033 Copyright © Teaching & Learning Company, Carthage, IL 62321

_____ has trouble understanding assignments, especially in _____. She doesn't grasp the basic concepts such as _____.

Let's work on this together so that she can fully comprehend this area by

_____

is untidy and disorderly, and the clutter is causing his grades to decline. If he were able to better organize, his grades would improve. This is nothing he is incapable of; as a matter of fact, he is a bright child with a slightly messy streak!

_____ has difficulty working independently of others. She seems dependent upon learning with the aid of another classmate. This may be because of low self-esteem, and in this case, I will try to boost her ego, because I know she is capable of working independently and doing a good job of it, too!

TLC10033 Copyright © Teaching & Learning Company, Carthage, IL 62321

_____

is good in math and easily understands its concepts and application. He is comfortable with numbers and grasps _____ well. His problem-solving ability and computation of numbers is excellent.

_____ is able to make realistic application in math with the use of a calculator and computer. She explores number ideas with ease and knows a broad range of content material. Her problem-solving and reasoning skills are superb.

_____

takes to numbers like old friends! Studying math is a pleasant experience for him. Please take the opportunity to build on our class lessons in _____ through activities with your child. A suggestion would be to _____.

_____ learned a new concept today in math. In our group lesson we discovered _____. There is a need for more individualization, so please go over this lesson again with your child tonight. Reinforcement to what we learned in class will help make sure it is understood.

TLC10033 Copyright © Teaching & Learning Company, Carthage, IL 62321

does not have a grasp of math. He struggles with the most basic of concepts. Please come in and talk about what we can do to improve his ability to apply math. Knowing and liking math can help his career opportunities in the future.

does not recognize regularities in numbers or the relationships of numbers. Please help your child in her recognition of what quantities equal each other so that she is more conversant with numbers.

is not able to visualize concepts such as multiplication and division. With the use of manipulatives like blocks or rods, you can help your child practice these simple concepts at home so that he can better grasp the lesson in school.

needs to be put at ease during math lessons. She is uncomfortable with the subject. Possibly we can talk one afternoon this week in order to come up with a solution that would make her feel more reassured when dealing with numbers.

_____

has not developed the ability to reason. It is important for him to learn this skill as it is closely tied to problem solving. You can help your child at home in this area by

_____.

_____

needs to go over the problems at home in the evening. Please help her review today's lesson in _____.
Math is sequential, and in order for her to understand the new lesson, she needs to understand the previous one.

_____

may need a math tutor. He is consistently bored with the subject, and something must boost his interest or he will not keep up with his classmates. It is important that he understand each new lesson so that he doesn't fall behind everyone else.

_____

needs to better understand fractions. She doesn't grasp the concept that a fraction is part of a whole. Please go over fractions at home by relating them to familiar aspects of your child's life. That way the concept will be better understood.

_170_

_____ seems to express himself

well through the use of _____.
type of material

His artistic creations are wonderful. Exposure to art museums

and books will lay the groundwork for a lifetime

of enjoyment in the field of arts.

_____

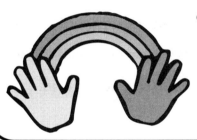

enjoys working in a variety of media. She understands color and

texture and seems to be a naturally gifted artist. One way to

encourage your child's love of art and talent is by helping her

pursue this interest and giving her support.

_____'s

appreciation of the natural environment can be seen in his

artwork. He has the ability to draw objects the way they look

in all their beauty and splendor. This will help in future

lessons on environmental science.

_____'s

ability in art is an important part of who she is and how she

sees herself. Please provide your child with as many out-of-

school experiences in this area as possible. May I suggest

_____.

_____

has fine motor skills and handles a pencil well. His hand-writing is good, and his papers are neat. Keep up the good work by helping your child practice handwriting at home, doing a variety of different exercises.

_____'s

handwriting is excellent. She forms the letters well, holds the pencil accurately and is writing sentences more speedily now. Her paper always looks attractive when she turns it in.

_____

is awkward with small motor tasks such as handwriting. His penmanship needs much work. Please practice with your child every night for 10 minutes because he does have the ability to succeed in this area.

_____

is artistically talented, however she has a difficult time learning to form her letters. Please provide plenty of instruction at home because extra practice will help make this problem disappear in time.

TLC10033 Copyright © Teaching & Learning Company, Carthage, IL 62321

_____
enjoys reading and treasures books. He is advanced in language skills and familiar enough with the alphabet that he takes naturally to reading.

_____
is a precocious child whose curiosity has enabled her to learn the alphabet quickly. Her careful observation has helped her to pick up reading naturally. She is easy to coach and a delight to work with in this area of study.

_____ is a slow reader and needs your help at home. There are two things you can actively do to insure your child's reading success. Have your child watch less television. Read to your child as much as possible so that he begins to have a larger vocabulary and starts enjoying language.

_____
is eager and happy to read. She is proud of her ability in this area and is always willing to read in front of the class. Encourage your child to read for pleasure and continue reading and enjoying books together!

TLC10033 Copyright © Teaching & Learning Company, Carthage, IL 62321

_____

loves to write. He is reflective with the information going on around him and knows how to organize it into a cohesive piece of writing. Your child does an excellent job at his writing assignments that require observing and thinking.

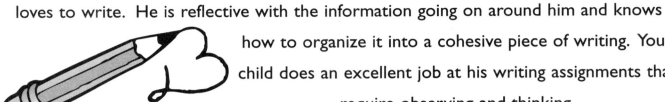

_____

enjoys writing about personal experiences. She writes about things in her life that are important to her. She writes with feeling and emotion. There is truth and realness in her writing.

_____

is a good writer. He focuses on interesting things and has good observational skills. He puts much more into his writing than simply cataloging detail. Encourage your child's writing ability at home by being helpful and supportive in this area.

_____ often complains that she has "nothing to write about" when we write in class. Selecting a topic is difficult for her. Then, as she writes, she struggles with words and sentences. Please practice writing exercises with your child for 10 minutes a night, such as_____.
Once writing becomes pleasurable, your child will have more success with it.

TLC10033 Copyright © Teaching & Learning Company, Carthage, IL 62321

_____

has excellent verbal expression for his age. He speaks well and seems confident in his use of the language. He is able to articulate his needs and responds to those around him in a clear style and concise manner.

_____ reverses her words and phrases and is unable to speak distinctly or express herself clearly. She rarely responds to instructions and may need more help than I can provide. Please call me at your earliest convenience so that we can discuss how to best go about assisting your child.

_____

is shy and often fears speaking. He is reluctant to contribute his ideas to class discussions, however he expresses himself well on paper. If he were to take pride in his thoughts, he would greatly add to the class.

_____

is being referred to a speech teacher. Your child has the following language problem:

_____ lisp   _____ stutter   _____ poor articulation

_____ other language disorder: _____

_____

TLC10033 Copyright © Teaching & Learning Company, Carthage, IL 62321

_____ is a good listener!

Keep up the verbal exchange in your lives.

He is able to listen and learn and learn by listening.

_____ listens courteously by taking turns and never interrupts others when they are speaking. She is good at following oral directions and at interacting with others. Her listening skills are excellent.

_____ listens only enough to learn what is being presented. After that he often ignores the speaker and goes off into his world. It is important that he learn to be a good listener and focus more on paying attention.

_____ is a poor listener. She rarely is still enough to listen to lessons. She talks and disrupts the class—if she would learn to listen, she would hear wonderful things and find out that it is fun and informative to hear what others have to say.

TLC10033 Copyright © Teaching & Learning Company, Carthage, IL 6232

_____

is naturally predisposed toward music. He loves sounds and rhythm and is responsive upon hearing sounds. He listens with enjoyment and attention. Your child may want to study an instrument at some point. If he does, I hope the opportunity to do so presents itself.

_____ has a musical talent.

She plays the _____ well and under- stands pitch, tones and rhythm better than many children her age. As I can see, music changes the way she feels and should be looked into further regarding future study.

_____

expresses himself well in music class. He loves to sing, dance, clap and move to rhythm. Singing is especially fun for him, and as a suggestion, you may want to sing these songs together at home _____ and _____. Have fun!

_____ would be a welcome addition to the school

____ band   ____ orchestra   ____ other: _____

The program will emphasize making music for enjoyment and the entertainment of others.

Please consider this request.

_____

is a good sport and gracefully accepts both victories and defeats. This wonderful quality of sportsmanship and cooperation is a trait that will carry over into all parts of his growing life.

_____

has excellent social skills on the playground. She has self-respect and respect for others. She shows sportsman-like conduct whether she's playing in a game or on the sidelines. What a delight to be around a person like this.

_____

has special athletic skills in _____.
His ability at the sport may be a source of recreational pleasure for many years to come, and it is suggested that he be encouraged in this area.

_____

has the strength, endurance, agility and vitality to pursue the sport of _____.
Her self-discipline in this area is remarkable. If she practices, she has the ability to be proficient in just a matter of time.

TLC10033 Copyright © Teaching & Learning Company, Carthage, IL 6232

Although _____

 is an average student in his lessons, he is proficient in the sport of

_____,

and this is an excellent outlet for building his self-image.

_____ is a good student

in class, however when she gets to the playground, she changes

into a competitive, selfish mood. She lacks the ability to share

and always wants to be first. Please call me next week, and

let's discuss a way of helping your child be more relaxed and friendly outdoors.

_____

 is a shy student and during time on the playground, often plays on

the sidelines. He is a less able athlete than others, yet he gives up

trying before he starts. With more self-confidence, I'm sure he

could find a sport in which he could excel.

_____ is wild during recess. She

is uncontrollable in a way that makes it difficult to teach her good sportsmanship and

cooperation. If she were to settle down somewhat, she

could have a great time. As it is now, she doesn't have the

opportunity to learn the positive effects of the playground.

_____ is doing good work in social studies. He understands the subjects being studied and brings with him more sophistication and experience to the topics taught. He is eager to learn and is a delight to have in class.

_____ is now learning the history of _____ and her intellectual level of understanding is well above other classmates. She excels in learning the subject matter presented and is an excellent student.

_____ knows how to use a map to locate places and can compare maps of the same area. Your child has a knack for building simple models of maps and can easily interpret symbols using a legend. He understands distance, direction and scale.

In social studies, _____ functions largely unaware of the other students in class. She does well independently, however, if someone tries to work with her or uses her supplies, she gets angry and pouts. Please call me so that we can discuss how your child might better fit in and enjoy the company of others.

TLC10033 Copyright © Teaching & Learning Company, Carthage, IL 6232

_____

has a good basic understanding in social studies. He is able to build on related concepts from one grade to the next. He is good at remem-bering dates, names and events.

_____ always reads her social studies lessons and makes an active attempt to join class discussions. She is a good example to other students and is articulate in expressing her viewpoint. When she is off the mark, she tries again until she feels successful.

_____

enjoys reading biographies of famous people. He likes the excite-ment and easily grasps the concept of how people go from a low point to a higher point in their lives. Reading biographies is an inspirational and productive way to spend time outside class.

_____

is learning social studies by memorization of facts and dates instead of by the examination of how people are influenced by their surroundings. If your child would simply try to under-stand the concepts, she would enjoy the subject more.

_____ is quick to pick up spelling words, even those that do not follow regular patterns. He has a rich list of words that he is proficient at spelling and does a good job of taking an active roll in class spelling lessons.

_____ is not only good at spelling, she is able to use the words as part of her vocabulary. Her skill in spelling and vocabulary exceed her age level. She will be kept challenged in class so that her love of spelling and vocabulary continue to grow.

_____ has made great improvement in spelling since _____.
The result is because he is becoming a better reader, and he sees the words directly applied in sentences.
Both you and your child should be very proud.

_____ is having difficulty in spelling.
This is not a sign of poor intelligence, it is because some children have trouble in this area. Please go over the following spelling words tonight:

_____, _____, _____, _____,

TLC10033 Copyright © Teaching & Learning Company, Carthage, IL 6232

_____'s

vocabulary is large and exceeds his age level. The range of
words known by your child is extraordinary. He uses new
words that constantly amaze me. Continue the rich use of language at home, where your child must be taking advantage
of so many wonderful words.

_____ absorbs words at a rapid pace.

She is constantly listening to the world around her and then
trying out new vocabulary words. Most of the time when she
uses words, they are used accurately. Continue to allow your
child to listen and absorb the words being said around her.

_____

has a rich vocabulary, however rarely contributes to class. Possibly he
needs more self-confidence so that he is able to voice his opinions and
not care what others think. Should he be able to do this, he would get
so much more out of his school experience.

_____

needs to work on vocabulary words—not just the memorization but their application.
Please go over the following words and definitions
tonight: _____

_____

LC10033 Copyright © Teaching & Learning Company, Carthage, IL 62321

_____

is doing much better work in the subject of

_____ because

_____ .

Keep up the good work!

_____

is not able to do good work in the subject of _____

because _____ .

Practice the following exercises at home:

_____

_____

always completes work well.

When assignments are turned in, the

presentation is neat and easy to read.

Good job!

_____

does not complete assignments. When homework is turned in, only part

of it is there. It is important that all assignments are finished

so that we can move on to the next lesson

knowing your child understood the last one.

TLC10033 Copyright © Teaching & Learning Company, Carthage, IL 6232

_____

completes independent assignments well.
When homework is given, the job gets done
and is completely self-directed.

_____

does not complete independent assignments.
When homework is given, the fear that it will not be done correctly
gets to your child, who then turns in incomplete work.

_____

is making excellent progress in _____.
This improvement is due to the extra work being done on assignments out of class.

Congratulations!

_____

is not making the progress hoped for in _____.

Keep practicing _____ and

doing the following exercises at home:

_____

C10033 Copyright © Teaching & Learning Company, Carthage, IL 62321

_____

puts forth the best of efforts in class.

This is done by taking part in class discussions,

listening with a strong intent to learn

and promptly handing in class assignments.

_____

does not put forth the best of efforts during class.

This could be improved by taking part in discussions

and listening better.

_____

tries very hard to _____.

Efforts being made to achieve this goal are wonderful.

Remember, all success comes with a few struggles!

_____

does not try hard enough at _____.

Efforts are minimal and much more hard work needs to

be done before improvement is possible. Try working on

this at home: _____

_____.

TLC10033 Copyright © Teaching & Learning Company, Carthage, IL 623

_____

carefully does work and gets it right the first time around.
Attempts made to complete and turn in good work are
always followed through.

_____

rushes through work to turn it in. Often work is sloppy
and difficult to read. It would be helpful to work on

_____

for 10 minutes a night at home.

_____

has the potential to _____ by

_____.

Keep an eye on breakthroughs in this area!

_____

has the potential to _____

however doesn't use resources around

to an advantage.

Please take notice of this.

_____

is eager to improve at

_____ and is trying

diligently by _____.

With this kind of enthusiasm, improvement should be soon noticeable.

_____

is not eager to improve at

_____.

This is too bad, because the potential is there. Working at home may help. Try this:

_____

_____

performs well with responsibilities.

The ability to act independently and make decisions

seems to be a natural one.

Official Proclamation

_____

could perform well with responsibilities,

yet doesn't have the ambition to do so.

It would be best for your child's attitude to improve. Here's an

idea: _____

TLC10033 Copyright © Teaching & Learning Company, Carthage, IL 62321

_____ takes part is class discussions and is active in voicing opinions. The other students in class have the utmost respect for this fine quality.

_____ doesn't take part in class discussions as regularly as is necessary. For more self-confidence and less fear of failure, I would suggest more interactions within the class.

✳ Part 3 ✳
Communication with Students Made Simple

If you thought communicating with parents would be a good form of relaying information and receiving gratification–try your students. Watch their eyes widen as you put a note in their hand or on their desk. Receiving a personalized note adds warmth to a school day, sunshine to a long afternoon.

In this section, you will find notes to hand out or send to your students. The thank-you notes express appreciation for something your student has done for you. The notes of regret plunge into an apology, yet remain genuine. The notes of concern acknowledge that you care. The notes of congratulations share your enthusiasm for outstanding work. Also included in this section are notes of inquiry, contracts for every subject area and end-of-year final thoughts.

What all of these notes to students have in common is a sincere tone. Almost all are emphasized by their brevity.

TLC10033 Copyright © Teaching & Learning Company, Carthage, IL 62321

_____

Thank you for lining up today.

You were very helpful in following the rules.

--------------------------- Cut here. ---------------------------

_____

Thank you for taking attendance.

You did a terrific job.

--------------------------- Cut here. ---------------------------

_____

Thank you for taking your seat.

You were helpful and polite.

--------------------------- Cut here. ---------------------------

_____

Thank you for washing the chalkboard.

You did a good job cleaning it.

_____

Thank you for watering the plants.

That was responsible of you.

------------------------------- Cut here. -------------------------------

_____

Thank you for running an errand.

Your efforts helped out when

they were needed.

------------------------------- Cut here. -------------------------------

_____

Thank you for collecting money.

You are very capable.

------------------------------- Cut here. -------------------------------

_____

Thank you for collecting workbooks.

You are dependable and organized.

TLC10033 Copyright © Teaching & Learning Company, Carthage, IL 62321

_____

Thank you for being room monitor.

You did a great job

handling your special duty.

- Cut here. -

_____

Thank you for being timekeeper.

You did an accurate job of keeping

track of the minutes.

- Cut here. -

_____

Thank you for being a leader today.

You have the ability to be number **1**!

- Cut here. -

_____

Thank you for helping

keep the room in order.

You can be counted on for being neat!

_____

Thank you for helping out the new student.

It was so nice of you

to show this person around school.

_____

Thank you for cooperating.

You made the day so much easier.

_____

Thank you for being considerate.

You are kind and thoughtful.

_____

Thank you for paying attention.

You listened to an important message.

TLC10033 Copyright © Teaching & Learning Company, Carthage, IL 62321

Thank you for raising your hand.

It was thoughtful of you to talk in turn.

Thank you for finishing your work.
You did a good job
completing the assignment.

Thank you for keeping your

hands and feet to yourself.

You were very polite today.

Thank you for assisting me today.

You are a dependable

and good worker.

TLC10033 Copyright © Teaching & Learning Company, Carthage, IL 62321

_____

Thank you for trying.
You put forth your best efforts.

------- Cut here. -------

_____

Thank you for listening so well.
You are learning more than ever!

------- Cut here. -------

_____

Thank you for taking your seat.
You were helpful and polite.

------- Cut here. -------

_____

Thank you for
teaching me a lesson.
You are bright and imaginative.

TLC10033 Copyright © Teaching & Learning Company, Carthage, IL 62321

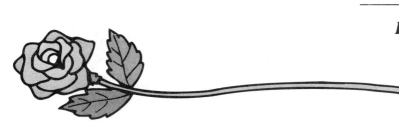

_____

I am sorry that I laughed at you.

That was not caring of me.

— Cut here. —

_____

I am sorry I teased you.

There is no excuse for what I did.

— Cut here. —

_____

I am sorry for embarrassing you.

I didn't mean to make you uncomfortable.

— Cut here. —

_____

I am sorry to have criticized you.

You deserve better
treatment than that.

TLC10033 Copyright © Teaching & Learning Company, Carthage, IL 62321

_____

I am sorry I lost my temper with you.

I shouldn't have been so rude.

Please forgive me.

-------------------------------- Cut here. --------------------------------

_____

I am sorry I got annoyed with you.

I didn't mean to take out on you what is bothering me.

-------------------------------- Cut here. --------------------------------

_____

I am sorry I wasn't fair.
I will be more impartial next time.

-------------------------------- Cut here. --------------------------------

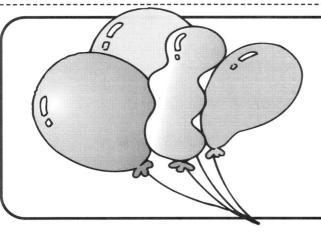

_____

I am sorry to have doubted you.
Next time you tell me something,
I will believe you.

TLC10033 Copyright © Teaching & Learning Company, Carthage, IL 6232

I am sorry I blamed you for something
that wasn't your fault.
That was rude of me.

Cut here.

I am sorry I accused you of
something you didn't do.

I will get more facts next time.

Cut here.

I AM SORRY I WAS NOT PATIENT WITH YOU.
I SHOULD HAVE BEEN MORE CALM.

Cut here.

I am sorry I punished you.
You were not at fault.
My apologies.

I am sorry I wasn't clear.

_I will be more specific
next time we talk._

-------------------- Cut here. --------------------

I am sorry I didn't call on you.
Next time you have your hand raised,
I will call on you first!

-------------------- Cut here. --------------------

_I am sorry I didn't listen
to what you were telling me.
That was inconsiderate of me._

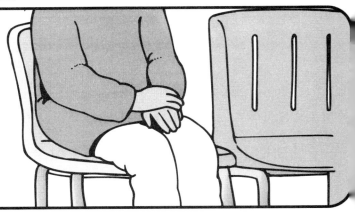

-------------------- Cut here. --------------------

_I am sorry I thought
you were wrong._

You were right.

TLC10033 Copyright © Teaching & Learning Company, Carthage, IL 6232

_____

I am concerned about your work in _____.

I think you could improve by _____

_____.

Please let me know how I can help you.

_____

I like having you in my class, and I am concerned that you haven't been yourself.

Is something wrong? Please come talk to me if you need to.

I CARE ABOUT YOU

_____

I believe that you are telling the truth.

I will stick with you through this difficult time and will be there to help you through it.

I CARE ABOUT YOU

_____

I want to meet you on _____,

to talk about _____.

Please mark this date on your weekly calendar.

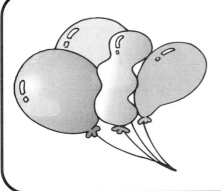

Sometimes you seem bored.

I want to make school fun for you.

Please let me know how I can do that.

------------------------------- Cut here. -------------------------------

I am here to help you with anything.

Don't be afraid to ask me.

I will take you seriously.

------------------------------- Cut here. -------------------------------

I understand you want your mother here today.

Sometimes it is tough being separated.

Let me know what I can do to make you more comfortable.

------------------------------- Cut here. -------------------------------

If you have a question, please ask.

Remember that every question asked is a good one.

TLC10033 Copyright © Teaching & Learning Company, Carthage, IL 6232

_____

You have a difficult problem to face.

If you need to talk to someone, I am here and will listen to you. You can trust me.

---- Cut here. ----

_____

You raised an important question.

A question that needs to be looked into further.

A question that requires an important answer.

Let me get back to you.

---- Cut here. ----

_____

You made a difficult choice today. Sometimes it's hard to pick one thing over another.

You should be proud of making a decision.

---- Cut here. ----

_____

I recognize your efforts and know that you are trying

extra hard to

_____.

Keep up the good work!

You're getting better at it all the time!

_____

You are an individual. You are one of a kind!

Be proud of yourself—you're great!

-------------------------------- Cut here. --------------------------------

_____

Is something on your mind? If you would like to talk, please come see me.

I will help any way I can.

-------------------------------- Cut here. --------------------------------

_____

If you ever need a hug or someone to hold you, let me know.

I'm here to make you feel as good as possible.

-------------------------------- Cut here. --------------------------------

_____

If the assignment on _____ was too hard, let's find a time to work on it together so that you understand. How about this day and time: _____ ?

TLC10033 Copyright © Teaching & Learning Company, Carthage, IL 62321

_____

Your work has been late.

Can I help you with something

so that it will be turned in on time?

Please let me know.

------------------------------ Cut here. ------------------------------

_____

If you are feeling bad about not being the best at

_____, remember how good you are

at _____.

Feel good about your abilities, not bad!

------------------------------ Cut here. ------------------------------

_____

I am your teacher, but I can be a friend if you need one.

Please come talk to me about anything. What you have to say is important to me.

------------------------------ Cut here. ------------------------------

_____

I appreciate you.

You have done some wonderful things in class this year, and I just wanted to tell you so.

Totally Awesome Work!

-------------------- Cut here. --------------------

You're a
Superstar!

-------------------- Cut here. --------------------

WOW!

You're Neat!

-------------------- Cut here. --------------------

You're Terrific!

TLC10033 Copyright © Teaching & Learning Company, Carthage, IL 62321

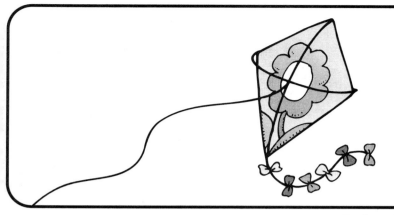

Keep up the
Good Work!

--- Cut here. ---

Much Better!

--- Cut here. ---

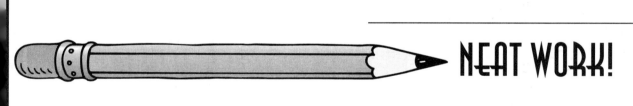

NEAT WORK!

--- Cut here. ---

You Are Bright!

TLC10033 Copyright © Teaching & Learning Company, Carthage, IL 62321

```
  94        33        78                17      21
+ 25      + 67      + 31              + 32    + 64
─────     ─────     ─────             ─────
 119       100       109                79
```

What Progress!

- Cut here. -

WELL DONE!

- Cut here. -

Good Effort!

- Cut here. -

Excellent!

TLC10033 Copyright © Teaching & Learning Company, Carthage, IL 6232

Big Improvement!

------- Cut here. -------

Very Creative!

------- Cut here. -------

Out of This World!

------- Cut here. -------

Your Organization Skills Are Improving!

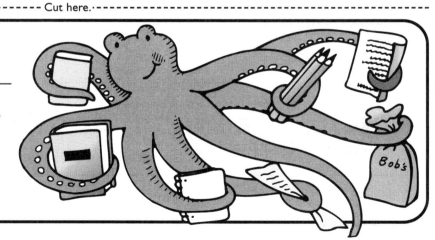

Good job for remembering to

_____

---- Cut here. ----

_____

You stuck to it . . . and did it!

---- Cut here. ----

_____

You should be proud of

_____

---- Cut here. ----

_____

You have a bright future in

_____

TLC10033 Copyright © Teaching & Learning Company, Carthage, IL 62321

 There Is a Great Change
in Your Work!

Cut here.

 **You Are a Leader!**

Cut here.

 **Corrected Work!**
Excellent!

Cut here.

Neat Handwriting!

Great Spelling!

---- Cut here. ----

Terrific Drawing!

---- Cut here. ----

Dictionary

Wonderful Vocabulary!

---- Cut here. ----

Cool Science Experiment!

TLC10033 Copyright © Teaching & Learning Company, Carthage, IL 62321

**Fantastic
Reading Project!**

--- Cut here. ---

**BIG
Improvement!**

--- Cut here. ---

EARTH SAVER AWARD

For helping _____

--- Cut here. ---

Homework Star!

What Are You Working on Now?

Please fill in the blanks and return this sheet when completed.

Date: _____

Dear _____,

What are you working on now? _____
_____

Tell me a little bit about the project. _____
_____

What do you hope to learn after this project is over? _____
_____

When is this project due?_____

Do you have enough time to work on it? Yes _____   No _____

Do you find the project interesting? Yes _____   No _____

It would be more interesting if_____
_____

The best parts of working on this are _____
_____.

My least favorite parts of the project are _____
_____.

Are you using extra books to help you? Yes _____   No _____

If so, which ones? _____
_____

When do you work on the project? _____
_____

Do you have any other comments? _____
_____

TLC10033 Copyright © Teaching & Learning Company, Carthage, IL 62321

What Do You Think About . . . ?

Please fill in the blanks and return this sheet when completed.

Date: _____

Dear _____,

What do you think about _____

_____

_____?

I think _____

_____

_____.

Where did you get your information (books, newspapers, friends, other)? _____

_____

_____

The action I would most like to take is _____

_____

_____.

The good things about it are _____

_____.

The bad things about it are _____

_____.

I would like to help by _____

_____.

Other comments: _____

_____

_____

_____

What Do You Want to Do About . . . ?

Please fill in the blanks and return this sheet when completed.

Date: _____

Dear _____ ,

What do you want to do about _____
_____
_____ ?

I want to _____
_____
_____ .

Outline your plans here. _____
_____
_____

How much time will it take you to do this? _____
_____

What do you hope to learn? _____
_____
_____

The good things about this will be _____
_____ .

The bad things about this will be _____
_____ .

Other comments: _____
_____
_____

216

What Do You Know About . . . ?

Please fill in the blanks and return this sheet when completed.

Date: _____

Dear _____,

What do you think about _____

_____

_____?

I know that _____

_____

_____.

How do you know this? _____

_____

_____

Can you tell me anything more? Yes ___ No ___

What? _____

Can someone you know tell me more? Yes ___ No ___

Who? _____

What do you think of the information that you have? _____

_____

_____

What will you do now that you have this information? _____

_____

_____

Do you have any other comments? _____

_____

_____

Homework Contract

Date: _____

I, _____, agree to do all my home-
⠀⠀⠀⠀⠀⠀⠀⠀⠀⠀⠀⠀student
work in _____ and will work on
⠀⠀⠀⠀⠀⠀⠀⠀⠀⠀⠀⠀⠀subject
it _____ each day at home.
⠀⠀⠀minutes
This contract is good until _____,
⠀⠀⠀⠀⠀⠀⠀⠀⠀⠀⠀⠀⠀⠀⠀⠀⠀⠀⠀⠀date
If I honor this contract until it is over and I receive a positive evaluation from my teacher, I will _____
_____.

Signed by _____
⠀⠀⠀⠀⠀⠀⠀⠀⠀⠀⠀⠀⠀⠀⠀⠀⠀⠀student
⠀⠀⠀⠀⠀⠀⠀⠀⠀⠀⠀_____
⠀⠀⠀⠀⠀⠀⠀⠀⠀⠀⠀⠀⠀⠀⠀⠀⠀⠀parent
⠀⠀⠀⠀⠀⠀⠀⠀⠀⠀⠀_____
⠀⠀⠀⠀⠀⠀⠀⠀⠀⠀⠀⠀⠀⠀⠀⠀⠀⠀teacher

- Cut here. -

Behavior Contract

Date: _____

I, _____, agree to improve my behavior by _____
⠀⠀⠀⠀⠀⠀⠀student
_____.

If I honor this contract until it is over and I have a positive evaluation from my teacher, I
will _____
_____.

If I don't honor this contract, I will _____
_____.

This contract is good until _____.

Signed by _____
⠀⠀⠀⠀⠀⠀⠀⠀⠀⠀⠀⠀⠀⠀⠀⠀⠀⠀student
⠀⠀⠀⠀⠀⠀⠀⠀⠀⠀⠀_____
⠀⠀⠀⠀⠀⠀⠀⠀⠀⠀⠀⠀⠀⠀⠀⠀⠀⠀teacher

GOOD BEHAVIOR

TLC10033 Copyright © Teaching & Learning Company, Carthage, IL 62321

Reading Contract

Date: _____

I, _____ , agree to read _____ pages
              student   number

of the book _____ by
                                book title

_____ and _____ more pages by _____ .
     date   number   date

When I finish reading the book, I will _____

_____ .

Signed by _____
                                   student

_____
                                   teacher

Reading Power

- - - - - - - - - - - - - - - - - - - Cut here. -

Parent-Partner Reading Contract

Date: _____

I, _____ , agree to read the book
               student

_____ with _____
          book title

by _____ .
          date

When we finish reading the book, we will _____

_____ .

Signed by _____
                                 student

_____
                                   parent

_____
                                   teacher

Reading Partners

Math Contract

Date: _____

I, _____, agree to do the following math:
      student

workbook pages: _____

homework assignments: _____

handout problems: _____

other: _____

by _____. If I honor this contract and the
      date

work I turn in is acceptable, I will _____

_____.

Signed by _____
                                  student

_____
                                  teacher

- Cut here. -

Science Contract

Date: _____

I, _____, agree to learn more about the topic of
      student

_____ in science class by the date of

_____. To do this, I will _____

_____.

I pledge to abide by this contract and do my best work.

Signed by _____
                                  student

_____
                                  teacher

TLC10033 Copyright © Teaching & Learning Company, Carthage, IL 62321

Social Studies Contract

Date: _____

I, _____, agree to learn more about the topic of
         student

_____ for social studies. To do this, I will _____

_____.

This contract is good until _____.

I pledge to abide by this contract and do my best work.

Signed by _____
                                    student

_____
                                    teacher

- Cut here. -

Spelling Contract

Date: _____

I, _____, agree to learn to spell the following words:
         student

_____   _____

_____   _____

_____   _____

_____   _____

I will know the spellings of these words by _____.

If I honor this contract and the work I turn in is acceptable, I will _____

_____.

Signed by _____
                                    student

_____
                                    teacher

ABCDEFG...

Writing Contract

Date: _____

I, _____ , agree to write _____

student

_____

_____

by the date of _____ .

If I honor this contract and the work I turn in is acceptable to the teacher, I will _____

_____

Signed by _____

student

_____

teacher

- Cut here. -

Vocabulary Contract

Date: _____

I, _____ , agree to learn the definitions of the following words:

student

_____   _____

_____   _____

_____   _____

_____   _____

I will learn them by _____ .

If I honor this contract and the work I turn in is acceptable, I will _____

_____ .

Signed by _____

student

_____

teacher

ABCDEFG...

TLC10033 Copyright © Teaching & Learning Company, Carthage, IL 62321

_____

It has been nice having you in my class this year.

------------------------------- Cut here. -------------------------------

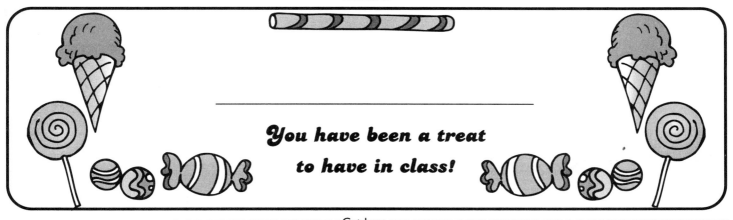

_____

You have been a treat to have in class!

------------------------------- Cut here. -------------------------------

_____

You have helped make this a magical year.

Thank you!

------------------------------- Cut here. -------------------------------

_____

Enjoy your summer and keep reading!

_____

During the summer, continue to

_____

-------------------------------- Cut here. --------------------------------

_____

Have a great move.
We'll miss you next year!

-------------------------------- Cut here. --------------------------------

_____

Stop by and say "hello" next year.

-------------------------------- Cut here. --------------------------------

_____

Thank you for your cooperation
throughout the year.

TLC10033 Copyright © Teaching & Learning Company, Carthage, IL 62321

∗ *Part 4* ∗

Communication with Administrators and Caretakers Made Simple

This last section includes notes to send to other professionals within the school–the principal, librarian, janitor, coach, nurse, school counselor or other teachers. Included are a variety of general notes designed for easy communication between yourself and these professionals.

Date: _____

Dear _____,

Please talk to this child for me. I am having difficulty getting through to

_____ regarding _____

_____.

Sincerely,

_____
teacher

Comments from Principal: _____

_____

_____

-- Cut here. --

Date: _____

Dear _____,

I want you to meet and recognize

_____.

This student has done an exceptional job at_____

_____.

_____'s efforts have assisted in the following ways:

_____.

Sincerely,

_____
teacher

TLC10033 Copyright © Teaching & Learning Company, Carthage, IL 62321

Date: _____

Dear _____,

I am sending in my student, _____, with an overdue book. It looks like it is _____ days late. Please take care of this matter today so that my student's records can be cleared up.

Sincerely,

_____
                    teacher

Late Notice

- Cut here. -

Date: _____

Dear _____,

Please help my student, _____, find a book on

_____.

A report is due entitled _____ and any research materials you have would be helpful.

Thank you!

Sincerely,

_____
                    teacher

Thanks

LC10033 Copyright © Teaching & Learning Company, Carthage, IL 62321

Date: _____

Dear _____,

    Please help my student,

_____,

    find a book about

_____.

This is a favorite reading subject of this student who wants to know more about the topic.

Thank you for your assistance.

Sincerely,

_____
teacher

Date: _____

Dear _____,

    Please help my student,

_____,

find some reading material that would be interesting. This is a student who does not enjoy reading but needs to read a book for _____

_____.

Thank you for your assistance.

Sincerely,

_____
teacher

Cut here.

TLC10033 Copyright © Teaching & Learning Company, Carthage, IL 6232

Date: _____

Dear _____,

Please do not erase the board. We need this material for tomorrow's lesson.

Thank you!

Sincerely,

_____
teacher

_____
room no.

-- Cut here. --

Date: _____

Dear _____,

Please keep our chairs in place.

We need them in this order for tomorrow's class.

Thank you very much!

Sincerely,

_____
teacher

_____
room no.

LC10033 Copyright © Teaching & Learning Company, Carthage, IL 62321

Date: _____

Dear _____,

Sorry about leaving such a mess!

We will not make a habit of it!

Thank you for being so understanding!

Sincerely,

_____
teacher

_____
room no.

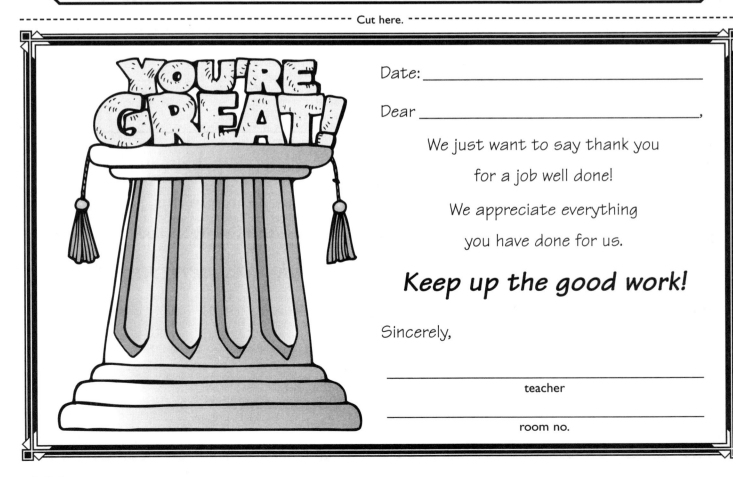

- Cut here. -

Date: _____

Dear _____,

We just want to say thank you

for a job well done!

We appreciate everything

you have done for us.

Keep up the good work!

Sincerely,

_____
teacher

_____
room no.

TLC10033 Copyright © Teaching & Learning Company, Carthage, IL 6232

Date: _____

Dear _____,

On _____,
         day and date

we plan to _____

_____.

If you think your students might enjoy the experience, please plan to bring them by around _____ o'clock so that our classes can enjoy this together.

Sincerely,

_____
                teacher

_____
                room no.

Date: _____

Dear _____,

Our class is celebrating _____

_____

on _____
         day and date

at _____ o'clock.

We plan to_____

_____.

Please bring your class to celebrate with us!

Bring _____.

Sincerely,

_____
                teacher

_____
                room no.

- - - Cut here. - - -

Date: _____

Dear _____,

Please excuse _____

from the following activity: _____

_____

because _____

_____,

**Thank your for your assistance
in this matter.**

Sincerely,

_____
teacher

_____
room no.

- Cut here. -

Date: _____

Dear _____,

_____
student

has done an exceptional job at _____

_____

and now needs to get exercise. I think physical activity would be good for this student.

Sincerely,

_____
teacher

_____
room no.

TLC10033 Copyright © Teaching & Learning Company, Carthage, IL 6232

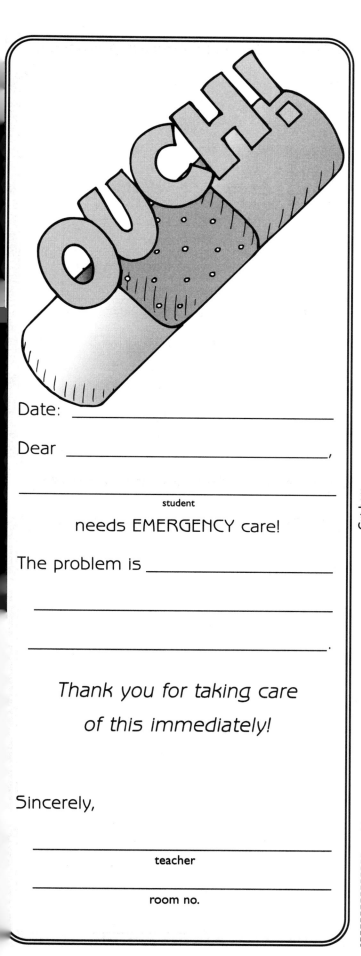

OUCH!

Date: _____

Dear _____,

_____
student

needs EMERGENCY care!

The problem is _____

_____

_____.

Thank you for taking care

of this immediately!

Sincerely,

_____
teacher

_____
room no.

------- Cut here. -------

Date: _____

Dear _____,

_____ has not
student

been feeling well since _____.

The symptoms are _____

_____

_____.

I hope you can do something
for this student.

Thank you for your assistance.

Sincerely,

_____
teacher

_____
room no.

Date: _____

Dear _____,

_____ needs an evaluation in the following area:

                  student

_____ self-esteem   _____ emotional development

_____ physical development   _____ daydreaming

_____ learning disabled   _____ underachievement

_____ gifted learning   _____ disadvantaged environment

_____ other: _____

Thank you for your assistance.

Sincerely,

_____
                 teacher

_____
                 room no.

- - - - - - - - - - - - - - - - - Cut here. - - - - - - - - - - - - - - - - -

Date: _____

Dear _____,

Please help with _____

_____

_____

_____.
                 student

is having trouble in this area and needs
some assistance from you.

Sincerely,

_____
                 teacher

_____
                 room no.

234

TLC10033 Copyright © Teaching & Learning Company, Carthage, IL 6232